D1234635

"Dipso"   from the painting by Louis Di Valentin

FRVIT of the VINE

AS SEEN BY MANY WITNESSES
OF ALL TIMES

BY

GRACE H. TURNBULL

2008

223 CHANCERY ROAD

BALTIMORE

MD.

PRINTED BY
THE LORD BALTIMORE PRESS
BALTIMORE 2, MD.

By the Same Author

TONGUES OF FIRE
Sacred Scriptures of the Non-Christian World
Johns Hopkins Press

THE ESSENCE OF PLOTINUS
Oxford University Press

"When a reformer stands alone he is a 'fanatic'; when there are several with him, they are 'enthusiasts'; when everybody is with him, he is a 'hero.'"

PREFACE

In many cases passages quoted in this book, though somewhat separated in the originals, have been printed here in closer sequence; or they have been condensed by the omission of phrases unimportant for the present purpose; though to avoid continually breaking up the pages with ellipses or asterisks such omissions have not been indicated except where it was demanded by the sense.

Such facts and statistics as have been used have been drawn from figures obtained from the Department of Commerce, Washington; from the FBI bulletins, or other authoritative sources, and the effort has been to have them as accurate as is humanly possible.

I acknowledge with gratitude the help obtained from the numerous authors and publishers who are duly credited throughout the book; I am also indebted to the Walters Art Gallery, Baltimore, for permission to include in it reproductions of two drawings by Gavarni, and to Mr. Louis di Valentin for allowing me to reproduce his painting Dipso.

G. H. T.

223 Chancery Road
Baltimore 18

CONTENTS

PART I

PART II

A CLOUD OF WITNESSES

CONTENTS—Continued

Liquor from A to Z

APPENDIX

Questions about Drinking Commonly Asked by High School Students
Answered

PART I

CHAPTER I

FROM TIME IMMEMORIAL

It was the year 538 B.C. The dazzling feast was spread, and Belshazzar, king of Babylon, with a thousand of his lords, with his wives and concubines, drank deep out of the gold and silver vessels his father Nebuchadnezzar had brought from the Temple in Jerusalem. And as he drank, his disordered imagination descried an accusing hand writing on the plaster wall "over against the candlestick" where all could see, "Thou art weighed in the balance and art found wanting. Thy kingdom is divided and given to the Medes and the Persians."

While he and his war-lords were besotted with drink, the enemy troops were stealing up. The city was seized, as Cyrus records, "without battle or fight," and "in that night was Belshazzar, King of the Chaldeans, slain."

In the fourth century B.C. the young Alexander, dynamic, magnetic, and often magnanimous, sets out from

Macedonia to conquer the whole of the then known world. He was not only a military genius, but under the distinguished guidance of Aristotle, his tutor, he had developed great interest in literature, metaphysics, and medicine, which he actually practiced.

Plutarch tells how he crosses the Hellespont with an army some thirty-five thousand strong, and defeats the troops of Darius at the river Granicus. Here, had it not been for Clitus, who killed one of the enemy in the very act of aiming a mighty blow with his scimitar at Alexander's head, the latter would have lost his life. He subsequently conquers Phœnicia and Egypt, Persia, Bactria and Bokhara, receives the submission of various princes of India, and chooses Babylon on the Euphrates as capital of his rapidly expanding empire which already stretches from the Ionian Sea to the Indus in India. Arabia, Carthage, Italy, and Spain are next to be added to the vast domain.

Alexander's knowledge of medicine, it seems, did not lead him to apply its principles to himself. For at Bokhara, while at supper, he and Clitus having drunk, Plutarch tells us, "to excess," a quarrel arises between him and the friend who had saved his life. Angry words pass; Alexander seizes a javelin from one of his guards and plunges it into the breast of Clitus who falls dead at his feet. Having come to himself, in an agony of remorse, Alexander "the Great" spends all night and next day stretched upon the ground, weeping like a girl.

One day, on returning from sacrifice to the gods, assembling at supper his friends and officers, Alexander offered a prize to the man who could drink the most. Promachus won by drinking four congii of unmixed wine, and received the victor's crown; "and in three days," Plutarch adds, "was dead." Of the other guests, forty-one died of this debauch, seized by a violent chill while still inebriated.

From Babylon Alexander planned to open a maritime route to Egypt around Arabia. Just before his admiral Nearchus was to leave with the fleet, Alexander gave him a magnificent banquet, after which, yielding to the instances of one Medius, he spent a day and a night drinking in his friend's quarters. A fever followed, and within a week the Conqueror of the World, conquered by his love of the vine, lay dead, at thirty-three; and the World Empire he had been at such pains to build fell apart like a house of cards.

A modern counterpart of Alexander's slaying of his friend is related in the Life of General Lew Wallace, author of Ben Hur. In his capacity of lawyer Wallace was called upon to convict of murder former senator Hannegan who, according to him, possessed "the singing soul of a Byron."

Hannegan and his brother-in-law, Captain John Duncan, had been drinking heavily in Hannegan's home. When they reached the disputatious stage, Mrs. Hannegan tried to separate her husband and her brother; but Duncan broke from her and slapped Hannegan in the face. Hannegan snatched a Spanish dagger from the wall and plunged it into Duncan's body. He staggered to a neighboring room and lay down to die, murmuring, "It was all my fault." Hannegan kissed the prostrate man in deep contrition for a murder inspired solely by alcohol.

"O," cries the seer of two thousand years ago, "how exceeding strong is wine! it causeth all men to err that drink it: and when they are in their cups, they forget their love both to friends and brethren, and a little after draw out their swords. Is not wine the strongest, that enforceth to do thus?"   —I Esdras, iii.

On September 28th, A.D. 1066, two opposing forces lay in wait before the battle of Hastings which was to decide the fate of England. The Saxons spent the night before the battle drinking and singing, the Normans in fasting and prayer. As the *Chronique de Normandie* has it, in its quaint old French: "Moult furent les Anglais celle nuit en grands reveaulx et chantaient et mangeaient et buvaient, ne onques autre chose toute la nuit ne firent!" The battle went against the English; William of Normandy was lord of the land.

In the World War of 1940, it was the French who had caroused. The council of ministers of the Vichy government called alcoholism the chief cause of the French army's collapse and the worst of France's four great problems. The Frenchman was said to have become the world's heaviest tippler, imbibing an average of two and a half quarts of alcoholic beverages a week compared with the German's pint and a quarter and the Briton's three quarters of a pint. (*Newsweek,* Sept. 2, 1940). Said General Pétain, "Our soldiers were drunk and could not fight. Since the victory of World War I the spirit of pleasure, of riotous living and drinking has prevailed over the spirit of sacrifice."

And so France fell to Germany.

Returning to England, in 1811, we find as Prince Regent George the Fourth. Remarkably handsome, and naturally gifted, at fifteen he was proficient in the classics, spoke fluently French, Italian and German, and showed considerable taste for music and the arts, so that his tutor, Bishop Hurd, could say of him that he would be "either the most polished gentleman or the most accomplished blackguard of Europe, possibly both."

Thackeray recounts how he speedily drifted toward the second alternative, becoming a glaring example of the power of the bottle in high places. As Prince of Wales he had for many years an income of upwards of half a million dollars, later largely increased; but he was always hopelessly in debt. In 1795 Parliament appropriated three million dollars to relieve him of his most pressing creditors, but he was soon in need of funds again to meet the expenses of a life that Thackeray calls "all fiddling, and flowers, and feasting, and flattery and folly." Meanwhile thousands of his subjects were on the verge of starvation and food was selling at famine prices.

Malmesbury tells how at his marriage the Prince "reeled into Chapel and hiccupped out his vows of fidelity," which, needless to say, were not kept. In 1830 he died, nothing in his life becoming him "like the leaving of it."

That he was partly the product of a dissolute age may be urged in extenuation of his follies; but man may choose to follow or to set the pattern for his time,—to play the puppet or be truly *man*.

Saturday, December 6th, 1941, was payday in Hawaii for American soldiers, sailors and marines. In Honolulu, where they went on leave, five hundred saloons, the greater number owned and operated by unnaturalized Japanese, were cannily offering them free drinks, while their officers were at a dinner where also, no doubt, liquor freely flowed. All was ripe for the attack,—the Japanese struck, the tragedy of Pearl Harbor, on the 7th of December, was the result;—several thousand young Americans needlessly sacrificed, battleships sunk and destroyed, "473 bomber planes reduced to pulp." Recognizing liquor to be the traitor here, the authorities immediately placed the saloons under military ban. They remained closed for a period of seventy-seven days.

Adolf Hitler was keenly alive to the demoralizing effects of alcohol, and rigidly restricted the drinking of alcoholic beverages in Germany, at the same time encouraging a free use of them to break the morale of the European countries he wished to dominate.

It matters little what the alcoholic drink,—toddy in India, vodka in Russia, pulque in Mexico, pernod in France, beer in Germany, whisky, wine, cocktails, high-balls, ale or rum,—it is all one. Lured by the immediate sense of release from care and conscience which they effect, since the beginning of the world kings and conquerors, peers and commoners, have cut short their conquests and sacrificed their careers, bowing their necks in voluntary, abject servitude to the most inhuman of tyrants, gradually to lose their own humanity in the tilt toward the beast. History has been altered, kingdoms and countries lost by the might of liquor alone.

From time immemorial man has endeavored to heighten his joy, drown his sorrows and anxieties, quiet his conscience, and forget his responsibilities and inhibitions by temporarily paralyzing with alcohol the cells of his brain which register anxiety and fatigue, and control judgment and conscience; only to find, when he has fully regained his wits, that his gaiety is gone, his anxieties are not solved, his conscience has more to accuse him for, the renounced responsibilities hang more heavily still.

From time immemorial the sounds of revelry have died out in distress, and the fruit of the vine has left behind it a trail of human wrecks innumerable. Upon hearing the shouts of revelry at the table of the Danish king, Horatio asks of Hamlet:

> What does this mean, my lord?
> *Hamlet:* The king doth wake tonight and takes his rouse,
> Keeps wassail, and the swaggering up-spring reels;
> And as he drains his draughts of Rhenish down,
> The kettledrum and trumpet thus bray out
> The triumph of his pledge.
> *Horatio:*   Is it a custom?
> *Hamlet:* Ay, marry is't;
> But to my mind, though I am native here
> And to the manner born, it is a custom
> More honour'd in the breach than the observance.
> This heavy-headed revel east and west
> Makes us traduc'd and tax'd of other nations:
> They clepe us drunkards, and with swinish phrase
> Soil our addition; * and indeed it takes
> From our achievements, though perform'd at height,
> The pith and marrow of our attribute.

Why Shakespeare should hold this view (for Hamlet is essentially Shakespeare in his outlook on life), will be shown in the next chapter.

---

* = *title.*

CHAPTER II

POETS AND THE TAVERN

The gods are just, and of our pleasant vices
Make instruments to plague us.
                              —King Lear, *V, iii.*

Under Queen Mary in 1555, all taverns, ale or beer houses were ordered to be closed "on Sonday or other festeyvall or hollyedaye duringe the several tymes of mattyns, high mass, and even songe, upon payne of ymprysonmente." In spite of this precautionary measure which one could wish duplicated today, in Shakespeare's time most of the arrests for crimes of violence still occurred in the alehouses, as is shown by the archives in the Public Records Office, Somerset House, on London's Strand. No wonder he could with such passion inveigh against the invisible but powerful spirit that took possession of men there:

O thou invisible spirit of wine, if thou hast no name to be known by, let us call thee devil! O God, that men should put an enemy in their mouths to steal away their brains! that we should, with joy, pleasance, revel and applause, transform ourselves into beasts! To be now a sensible man, by and by a fool, and presently a beast! O strange! Every inordinate cup is unblest, and the ingredient is a devil . . . I could well wish courtesy would invent some other custom of entertainment.   —*Othello,* II, iii & ii.

In *Twelfth Night* Shakespeare asks and answers,

What's a drunken man like?
Like a drowned man, a fool and a madman: one draught
above heat makes him a fool; the second mads him; and a
third drowns him.   —I, v.

The career of one of Shakespeare's great contempo-
raries, Robert Greene, whose "only care was to haue
a spel in his purse to coniure up a good cuppe of wine
with at all times" was early wrecked by dissipation.
Poet, playwright and pamphleteer, one of the most
versatile and prolific writers of the day, Greene was
at first a striking figure in his elegant doublet and "very
faire Cloake with sleeues, of a graue goose turd greene."

Soon he was headed down hill: "Who in London
hath not heard of his dissolute, and licentious liuing?
his beggarly departing in euery hostisses debt; his obscure lurking in basest corners: his pawning of his
sword, cloake, and what not?"

At last he is picked up on the street, the Great Pox
syphilis racking his bones, and lies dying in the house
of a shoemaker and his wife who have befriended him;
and from his deathbed he writes to his deserted wife:
"That I haue offended thee highly I know, that thou
canst forget my iniuries I hardly beleeue: yet perswade
I my salfe if thou saw my wretched state, thou couldst
not but lament it. For my contempt of God, I am
contemned of men: for my gluttony, I suffer hunger:
for my drunkennesse, thirst: for my adulterie, ulcerous
sores." *

---

* *So Worthy a Friend: William Shakespeare,* by Charles Norman.

Milton allegorizes the effects of "orient liquor" offered to the weary traveler by Comus, god of revelry,
thus:

> —which as they taste
> (For most do taste, through fond intemperate thirst)
> Soon as the potion works, their human countenance,
> Th' express resemblance of the gods, is chang'd
> Into some brutish form of wolf or bear,
> Or ounce or tiger, hog or bearded goat,
> All other parts remaining as they were;
> And they, so perfect is their misery,
> Not once perceive their foul disfigurement,
> But boast themselves more comely than before,
> And all their friends and native home forget,
> To roll with pleasure in a sensual sty.
>
> —*Comus, A Mask,* 64-77.

In 1782 the blithe Bobby Burns, the laureate poet,
the Don Juan of his day, among the youth of the
countryside *facile princeps,* proposes this care-free toast
to his hero John Barleycorn:

> John Barleycorn was a hero bold,
> Of noble enterprise;
> For if you do but taste his blood,
> 'Twill make your courage rise.
>
> 'Twill make a man forget his woe;
> 'Twill heighten all his joy:
> 'Twill make the widow's heart to sing,
> Though the tear were in her eye.
>
> Then let us toast John Barleycorn,
> Each man a glass in hand:
> And may his great posterity
> Ne'er fail in old Scotland!

(We miss the tuneful singer here who could tenderly mourn the Mountain Daisy torn from its humble bed, and immortalize the Mouse. It would seem that the nature of the subject has drawn down with it the quality of his verse.) By 1790 Burns' praise of John Barley-corn has changed to warning:

> O Tam! hadst thou but been sae wise
> As ta'en thy ain wife Kate's advice!
> She tauld thee weel thou wast a skellum,
> A blethering, blustering, drunken blellum;
> That frae November till October,
> Ae market-day thou was nae sober. . . .
> That at the Lord's house, ev'n on Sunday,
> Thou drank wi' Kirton Jean till Monday.
> She prophesy'd that, late or soon,
> Thou would be found deep drown'd in Doon;
> Or catch'd wi' warlocks in the mirk,
> By Alloway's auld haunted kirk. . . .
>
> Now, wha this tale o' truth shall read,
> Ilk man and mother's son take heed:
> Whene'er to drink you are inclined, . . .
> Think, ye may buy the joys owre dear—
> Remember Tam o'Shanter's mare.
> —From *Tam o'Shanter*.

Had Burns heeded his own warning, his letter to his friend Robert Ainslee in November, 1791, would never have been written. He who had sung,

> For a big-bellied bottle's the whole of my care!

was to experience the reverse side of this care:

My dear Ainslee,—Can you minister to a mind diseased? Can you, amid the horrors of penitence, regret, remorse, headache, nausea, and all the rest of the d----d hounds of hell that beset a poor wretch who has been guilty of the sin of drunkenness—can you speak peace to a troubled soul? *Misérable perdu* that I am, I have tried everything that used to amuse me, but in vain: here must I sit, a monument of the vengeance laid up in store for the wicked, slowly counting every tick of the clock as it slowly, slowly numbers over these lazy scoundrels of the hours. . . . There is none to pity me. My wife scolds me, my business torments me, and my sins come staring me in the face.

To Mrs. Dunlop, Jan. 2, 1793:

Occasional hard drinking is the devil to me. Against this I have again and again bent my resolution, and I have greatly succeeded. Taverns I have totally abandoned: it is the private parties among the hard-drinking gentlemen of this country that do me the mischief.

"Totally abandoned" taverns! It was from the "King's Arms" tavern that he was returning early one morning after a debauch that he saw his worthy neighbor George Haugh who had risen earlier than usual to work. Though excited by the liquor he had drunk, he was able to articulate, "O George, you are a happy man. You have risen from a refreshing sleep, and left a kind wife and children, while I am returning a self-condemned wretch to mine." This is the man who had once written on a goblet,

> There's death in the cup—sae beware!
> Nay, more—there is danger in touching:

and

> See Social Life and Glee sit down,
> All joyous and unthinking,
> Till, quite transmogrified, they're grown
> Debauchery and Drinking.
> —From *Address to the Unco Good.*

His health is failing, and his death is hastened by an episode on a January night of 1796, when he had lingered till a late hour at the "Globe" tavern in Dumfries. He was overcome with drowsiness on his way home because of drink, and sank down in the deep snow where he slept for several hours. He contracted a rheumatic fever from which he never recovered. R. L. Stevenson says of him:

His death in his thirty-seventh year was indeed a kindly dispensation. That drink and debauchery helped to destroy his constitution and were the means of his unconscious suicide, is doubtless true. He had trifled with life and must pay the penalty. He had grasped at temporary pleasure and substantial happiness had passed him by.

His *Tragic Fragment* is tragic indeed:

O injur'd God! Thy goodness has endowed me
With talents passing most of my compeers,
Which I in just proportion have abus'd,
As far surpassing other common villains
As Thou in natural parts hadst given me more.

The tavern again plays a preponderating part in the pitiful career of that fantastic genius, Edgar Allan Poe. We follow his vacillating and vagrant course through the drawing rooms, bar-rooms and taverns of his day with immense indignation, not so much at his inability to resist the temptation to drink as at the stupidity of a society, fully aware of the danger, which yet tolerates the sale and circulation of this liquid death.

Says Poe of a stay in Richmond: "I certainly did give way to the temptation held out on all sides by the spirit of Southern conviviality. My sensitive temperament could not stand an excitement which was an every-day matter to my companions. In short, it sometimes happened that I was completely intoxicated. For some days after each excess I was invariably confined to bed." Again, "I drank—God only knows how often and how much."

As a consequence of his addiction to drink and opium he suffered agonies "more, I believe, than have often fallen to the lot of man. How much they have been aggravated by my consciousness that, in too many instances, they have arisen from my own culpable weakness or childish folly!" "*Nothing* cheers or comforts me. My life seems wasted—the future looks a dreary blank."

In Washington on the evening of Poe's arrival there to lecture and have an interview with the President, at a party at the Fuller House in which port wine figured prominently, the host, who would not be denied, over-persuaded Poe to drink. The next day he was ill; and later a roaring mint-julep party killed his last chance of lecturing or receiving the hoped-for political appointment. By nature particularly meticulous in his dress, he horribly embarrassed his friends by wearing his clothes inside out, and left the city he had reached full of anticipation in debt and empty of purse.

Once more in Richmond among his boyhood friends and associations he gives way to drink, disappearing for two weeks into an abandoned quarter of the town.

A friend wrote "Now no influence was adequate to keep him from the damnable propensity to drink." In Philadelphia, his imbibings brought on an utter collapse, an attack of delirium tremens, and landed him for a night in prison.

It was inevitable that Poe's subjection to drink should be reflected in his later works:

There is no trace, in these, of the brilliant and often solid workmanship of his better moments. The stories are ill-conceived and written carelessly. He seems to have lost respect for himself, for his art, and for his audience. . . . He who could write *King Pest* had ceased to be a human being.
     —R. L. Stevenson, *The Works of Edgar Allan Poe.*

On the eve of his proposed marriage to Mrs. Shelton, the round of parties and entertainments in Richmond made it impossible for him not to take what was pressed upon him, and in the resulting illness he was warned by his physician that another indulgence would spell death.

At last in Baltimore Poe took the fatal drink, and was picked up in front of a tavern much the worse for wear. A doctor who knew him was called and found him in the bar-room surrounded by ruffians.

His face was haggard, not to say bloated, and unwashed, his hair unkempt, his whole physique repulsive. His expansive forehead and those mellow, yet soulful eyes for which he was so noticeable when himself were shaded from view by a rusty, almost brimless, tattered and ribbonless palm leaf hat. He wore neither vest nor neckcloth, and the bosom of his shirt was crumpled and badly soiled.

This, then, was the man whom Mrs. Osgood could never forget, "with his proud beautiful head erect, his dark eyes flashing with the electric light of feeling and of thought, a peculiar, an inimitable blending of sweetness and hauteur in his expression and manner;" whom Professor Gildersleeve thought wonderfully handsome, "a poetical figure, if there ever was one, clad in black—slender—erect—the subtle lines of the face fixed in meditation." This the genius of whose best works the editor John Daniel could say that they were "coins stamped with the unmistakable die. They are of themselves; *sui generis,* unlike any diagram in Time's kaleidoscope, either past, present, or to come—and gleam with the hues of Eternity."

Poe was taken to Washington College Hospital (now the Church Home and Infirmary) where, delirious and obsessed by spectres, he said that "the best thing his friend could do would be to blow out his brains with a pistol—that when he beheld his miserable degradation he was ready to sink into the earth." Later he asked the doctor's wife who was ministering to him if there were any hope for a wretch like him beyond this life. Delirium tremens followed; then, after a period of quiet, he cried, "Lord help my poor soul!" A strange and unearthly genius, through man's stupidity, lay dead long before his time.*

With reverent pity for the tortures of this storm-tossed soul, to Poe's last anguished prayer we utter a fervent Amen. Bitter reproaches are often aimed at the pathetic victims of inebriety; disorderly drunkenness

---

*For the above material on Poe, I am very largely indebted to the biography entitled *Israfel,* by Hervey Allen. Farrar & Rinehart.

is an offence punishable by law. But what of the greater offence of the distiller who produces, the retailer who purveys, and the hostess who smilingly proffers to her guests the pernicious drink?

It is perhaps not generally known that Poe's older brother Henry, strangely resembling him in appearance, charm, imagination and gift for verse, as well as in the fatal weakness for drink, even earlier than Edgar failed in health. In 1831 Edgar wrote that Henry was "entirely given over to drink." Two years later the Great Killer carried him off at the age of twenty-four.

Poe's tragic story is largely duplicated in that of the writer-composer of the imperishable folk-songs that are nearest the hearts of all of us and seem to have grown out of the very soil of the Old South. Stephen Collins Foster, whose *Old Folks at Home, Swanee River, Massa's in de Cold, Cold Ground, Old Kentucky Home,* have echoed the country over, could not deliver himself of the habit "against which he wrestled with earnestness indescribable, resorting to all remedial expedients which professional skill or his own experience could suggest." At last in New York, separated from his wife and friends, he reached the lowest depths of poverty and degradation.

Mrs. Parkhurst Duer tells of her first meeting there with Foster thus:

I was engaged in a large music publishing house on Broadway, leading a very busy life, although but twenty-one years of age. Every day I met composers, and was hoping that Stephen Foster would appear; his songs had created within me a feeling of reverence for the man. One day the door opened, and a poorly dressed, very dejected-looking man came in, and leaned against the counter near the door. He looked ill and weak. No one spoke to him. A clerk laughed and said: "Steve looks down and out." I asked, "Who is that man?" "Stephen Foster," the clerk replied. "He's a vagabond, don't go near him."

I was terribly shocked. Forcing back the tears, I waited for that lump in the throat which prevents speech to clear away. I walked over to him, put out my hand, and asked, "Is this Mr. Foster?" He took my hand and replied: "Yes, the wreck of Stephen Collins Foster." "Oh, no," I answered, "not a wreck; but whatever you call yourself, I feel it an honour to take by the hand the author of 'Old Folks at Home.' I am glad to know you." As I spoke the tears came to his eyes, and he said: "Pardon my tears, young lady, you have spoken the first kind words I have heard in a long time. God bless you." I judged him to be about forty-five years of age, but the lines of care upon his face, and the stamp of disease, gave him that appearance. He was actually only thirty-seven.

We had a long conversation. I said if he would bring me his manuscript songs that he had not been able to write out, I would do the work for him at his dictation. He was very grateful, and from that time until he died I was permitted to be his helper. When he brought me his rude sketches, written on wrapping paper picked up in a grocery store, and told me he wrote them sitting upon a box or barrel, I knew he had no home.

Another friend describes his death as follows:

Early one winter morning I received a message saying that my friend had met with an accident; I dressed hurriedly and went to 15 Bowery where Stephen lived, and found him lying on the floor in the hall, blood oozing from a cut in his throat and with a bad bruise on his forehead. Steve never wore any night-clothes, and he lay there naked and suffering horribly. He had wonderful big brown eyes and they looked up at me with an appeal I can never forget. He whispered, "I'm done for," and begged for a drink; but the doctor who had been sent for arrived and forbade it.

We put his clothes on him and took him to the hospital. When I went back again the next day they said, "Your friend is dead." His body had been sent to the morgue, among the nameless dead. The next day his brother and widow arrived. When Mrs. Foster entered the room where Steve's body was lying, she fell on her knees before it, and remained for a long time.*

Alexander the Great, his friend Clitus, George the Fourth, Robert Greene, Burns, Henry and Edgar Allan Poe, Stephen Foster, Senator Hannegan and Captain Duncan,—these were not evil, were not stupid men; rather, most of them were peculiarly endowed. But they were mistaken in that they thought, like you perhaps, that they could keep their liquor under control; till liquor, turning, began to manhandle them, bringing upon them failure and degradation, or crimes which in their earlier days they would not have believed possible.

It is touching and heartening to find a later, greater poet than Poe fighting manfully and successfully against a similar servitude:

I have this day, this hour, resolved to inaugurate for myself a pure, perfect, sweet, clean-blooded, robust body, by ignor-

---

* *Stephen Collins Foster,* by Harold V. Milligan. Published by G. Schirmer, Inc.

ing all drinks but water and pure milk, and all fat meats, late suppers—a great body, a purged, cleansed, spiritualized, invigorated body.

—Entry in Walt Whitman's note-book, April 16, 1861.

From such a vow made in all solemnity before the altar of the inner sanctuary, and duly written down, so that one may be reminded of it from time to time, much help might be gained. The laws of human nature, the laws of God, cannot be circumvented. *What a man soweth that shall he also reap. If of the flesh he sow corruption, he shall also reap corruption.*

As it has been from time immemorial, so it is today: the taverns and saloons, increasing at an appalling rate, are a prolific, if not the chief source of crime. From a large box of items treating of alcohol-induced crime clipped from the morning edition of the Baltimore *Sun* in the last two or three years, let us choose the following:

Oct. 1, 1946: One Educator Is Slain, Second Shot during the cocktail hour in the "Ship's Tavern" of the famous old Brown Palace Hotel, Denver.

Mar. 10, 1947: Charged with fatally shooting his wife in a crowded tavern yesterday, J---- D---- was held without bail in Northwestern Police Court.

July 21, 1947: Injured in a tavern fight Saturday, W---- K---- died last night at Franklin Square Hospital.

Oct. 27, 1948: For biting off part of another man's ear in a tavern at Eastern Ave. and Oldham St., L---- W---- was sentenced to six months in the House of Correction.

Dec. 23, 1948: A gun battle of more than an hour's duration at a Henrico County night club early today ended in the death of two persons and the wounding of a third.

Jan. 26, 1949: Physicians at Mercy Hospital last night took eighty stitches to close razor-blade cuts which J---- S---- received in a Gay St. tavern in an altercation with a customer.

Jan. 29, 1949: Two men were shot and killed today in a near-by roadhouse in what Coroner Gray called murder and suicide. A third man was shot in the finger.

"O thou invisible spirit of wine, if thou hast no name to be known by, let us call thee devil" indeed! This same devil is the moving spirit behind innumerable instances from the daily paper of murder of friend by friend, of kith by kin, that match Alexander's slaying, some two thousand years ago, of the friend who saved his life.

The shoeless body of Mrs. B---- G----, a bride of a month, was found today doubled up in the trunk of her automobile, and her husband was taken into custody for questioning. The captain of the Essex County prosecutor's detectives quoted the dead woman's husband as saying that he and his wife had consumed a bottle of whiskey in their auto after stopping at various places for drinks, and that later they had quarreled over drinking.

—*The Sun,* Baltimore, Dec. 6, 1947.

A young mother walked into the police station today and signed a statement that she killed her brother-in-law. Her husband is now serving a life-term for the fatal shooting of his brother. The young woman said her husband took the blame for the shooting, which occurred after a drinking party, because she had an infant child to care for.

—*The Sun,* Baltimore, June 7, 1948.

CHAPTER III

THE PRESIDENTS TAKE THE STAND

GEORGE WASHINGTON
(1732–1799)

While Washington, living in a bibulous age, was not an abstainer himself, like many a drinker of our day, he was keenly alive to the advantage of having others abstain on whom he wished to depend. Concerning the good behavior of officers, he wrote to Governor Dinwiddie, April 18, 1756:

I can call my conscience, and what, I suppose, will be a still more demonstrative proof in the eyes of the world, my orders, to witness how much I have, both by threats and persuasive means, endeavored to discountenance gaming, drinking, swearing, and irregularities of every other kind.

Again to Governor Dinwiddie, Sept. 23, 1756:

I apprehend it will be thought advisable to keep a garrison always at Fort Loudon; for which reason I would beg leave to represent the number of tippling houses as a great nuisance to the soldiers, who, by this means, in despite of the utmost care, are, so long as their pay holds out, incessantly drunk, and unfit for service.

The first year of his command of the Continental Army, he issued an order, March 25, 1776:

All officers of the Continental Army are enjoined to assist the civil magistrates in the execution of their duty, and to prevent, as much as possible, the soldiers from frequenting tippling houses.

He could put teeth in his orders:

Any soldier found drunk shall receive one hundred lashes, without benefit of a court-martial.

All persons whatever are forbid selling liquor to the Indians. If any sutler or soldier shall presume to act contrary to this prohibition, the former shall be dismissed from camp and the latter receive severe corporal punishment.

To Thomas Green, carpenter at Mt. Vernon, Mar. 31, 1789:

—Drink is the source of all evil, and the ruin of half the workmen in this Country. Were you to look back and had the means to ascertain the cost of the liquor you have expended it would astonish you. In the manner this expense is generally incurred, that is by getting a little now, a little then, the impropriety of it is not seen; in as much as it passes away without much thought. But view it in the aggregate, you will be convinced at once, whether any man who depends upon the labour of his hands not only for his own support, but that of an encreasing family, can afford such a proportion of his wages to that article.

But the expense is not the worst consequence that attends it, for it naturally leads a man into the company of those who encourage dissipation and idleness by which he is led by degrees to the perpetration of acts which may terminate in his Ruin; but supposing this not to happen, a disordered frame, and a body debilitated, renders him unfit to discharge

To End Drunken
...ving Is Demanded

... March 18 (AP)—
...aw enforcement against
...who drive was demanded
...the National Committee
...c Safety.
...ing a nation-wide effort,
...mittee agreed to ask the
...dustry to get behind it.
...same time, the committee
...downward trend in auto-
...aths in general since 1941
...c rate was twelve deaths
...00.000 miles of travel. In
... death rate was. 8.1,
... deaths dropp...

...sh Drink Bill
...rally Reaches
...aggering Point

...Sun May 9

By JANETTA SOMERSET
...don Bureau of The Sun
...don, May 8—The time and
...y the British spend drinking
...d up, make fine propaganda
...he temperance societies. Some
...rmers complain of British
...king habits on moral grounds
...ne on financial.
...Leaving the moral issue or one
...the financial aspect is. to say

Sentenced
...hisky Counts

...erms ranging from two
...onths and fines up to
... imposed in Federal
...erday on seven men who
...ility to operating illicit
...ssessing untaxed whisky
...aviest penalty was im-
...Thomas Dawkins, Negro,
...siles, who admitted op-
...100-gallon still and pos-
... gallons of mash and 18
... untaxed whisky last
... near Huntsville, Prince
...unty. Dawkins was sen-
...eight months' imprison-
...fined $800.
...Scott and Lonzie Mayo.
...es, of Washington, also
...ilty to the same charges.
... sentenced to three
... prison and fined $600.
... was ...

The Christian Science Monitor calls attention to the fact

REPEAL DID NOT CLOSE ILLICIT STILLS

...that a report has just been issued by the U. S. Alcohol Tax
Unit of the Bureau of Internal Revenue which shows that in
1945 the unit destroyed 7,521 stills and arrested 9,492 per-
...sons attending them; attached two million dollars' worth of
...property where illicit liquor was stored, and confiscated
$169,000 worth of illegal ...

1946

...perating a
...till and possessing 150
...ome
...mash January 7 near his
...ntsville, Prince Georges

...el Chambers was sen-
...six months' imprison-
...ined $600, and Alphonzo
...n, Negro, was given a
... term and fined $600 for
... a 50-gallon still near
...ce Georges county, De-

...alties were meted out by
...ge William C. Coleman
...Court. C. Ross McKen
...y United States atto
...cuted the cases.

Americans Spend
$9,600,000,000 On
Alcoholic Drinks

From Sun, June 11, '46

Washington, June 10 (AP)—Americans spent a record $9,600,000,000
on alcoholic drinks last year, the
Commerce Department reported tonight.

That works out to an average
outlay of $66.66 a person among a
population of 144,000,000...
July 1, or ...

Congressmen Drink Too Much,
Washington Psychiatrist Says

N.Y. Times — Aug. 13, 1945

By The United Press

WASHINGTON, Aug. 12 (UP)—
Dr. Michael M. Miller, St. Elizabeth Mental Hospital psychiatrist
who is pioneering a new type clinic
for alcoholics, contended tonight
that alcohol is a damaging factor
in American legislation and diplo-
macy.

Dr. Miller, neither a prohibition-
ist nor a teetotaler, charged in an
interview today that too many
Congressmen are not moderate in
their drinking habits and that a
few are definite alcoholics and that
some ...

St...
...ler is
...insti...
...whic...
...mak...
...He
...fact

...most damaging effect on legislation."

He also charged that the State
Department and the United States
diplomatic corps are "stuffy with
drunks," and that foreign embas-
sies find liquor to be "the most
potent weapon in foreign policy
when dealing with Americans."

"The 'inebriating impulse' is a
prerequisite for the State Department and the diplomatic corps,"
he said.

His views were promptly and
vigorously challenged by members
of Congress. They generally la-
...beled as "grossly un-

Public Drinking
By Women Hit

Special to The News-Post

LOS ANGELES, Dec. 5—By
drinking in public bars, women
not only are losing their self-
respect, but are setting a bad
example for the coming generation.

Those who are mothers are
losing moral control over their
own children, as well.

They should be banned from
public drinking places.

William Louis Ritzi, chief of
the district attorney's juvenile
division, so declared today—and
offered proof to back up his
stand.

CASE CITED

At random he plucked out a
case from his voluminous files.
Ritzi said:

"This one shows that police
investigated neighborhood reports of a child being neglected.
When they arrived, this is what
they found:

"A nine-year-old girl, in a
tattered, dirty dress and a
sniffling cold

house. Cigaret butts floated
atop curdled cream in coffee
cups on the fly-infested table.

"Dishes on the table, and in
the sink all were dirty. Only
a quarter-pound of stale meat
was in the ice box. But no
milk.

"'Where is your mother?' the
police asked.

"'I guess she's down at the
corner cocktail bar,' came the
reply.

FOUND IN BAR

"Police found her there, sod-
den drunk, and surrounded by
a group of alcoholic bums.
They took her to jail; her
daughter to juvenile hall.

"I might add that 80 per
cent of children in juvenile hall
are from broken homes; 50 per
cent of broken homes are due
to drinking, and at least half of
them by mothers spending their
time in bars, when they should
be home.

"Let's stop this sort of
...ng, before it gets even to
..."

---

4 Girls Missing;
Police Hold Man

Anderson, S.C., May 19 (AP)—A
...ory of a twilight swim in under-
...clothes was told today as a search
went on for four missing school-
girls.

Jimmy Lee Elgin, 40, ice-plant
laborer, told about the swimming
party. He's in jail for questioning.

He was picked up by police early
today. In his automobile were girls'
wet underclothes.

He told Sheriff Clint McClain
that he had a date with Dorothy
Hawkins Redding, 14, but two other
girls joined the party. They were
Bobby Jean Ridley, 14, and her
sister, Marion, 12.

After a round of beers, Elgin told
the sheriff, the four decided to go
for a swim in the river at a spot
18 miles from here. After splash-
ing about for a while, they took off
their wet garments and donned
their outer ones.

STUDENT DRINKING
SEEN ON INCREASE

**Head of Wellesley Says it Poses
New Educational Problem'
—Parents a Factor**

College students are consuming
...more alcoholic drinks today than
formerly and creating a new problem for education, Mildred McAfee
Horton, president of Wellesley College, reported yesterday.

"Although the town of Wellesley
is dry and so is the college, the
girls at home and away from college are drinking more than they
...ed to do," she told 750 women
...nding the annual luncheon
New York Welle...
... the Bo...

SEDUCED, SAYS
DOCTOR'S WIFE

**She Tells Jury How Husband
Got Into Fatal Fight**

Cedar Rapids, Iowa, May 16 (AP).
—Mrs. Sydney Rutledge, her eyes red
from weeping, told the jury late
today she was seduced by the man
her husband is accused of killing.

The wife of Dr. Robert C. Rutledge, Jr., told how her acquain-
tanceship with Byron C. Hattman
ripened into friendship. Her husband, a 28-year-old St. Louis children's specialist, is accused of
fatally stabbing Hattman here last
December 14.

She said she went on two sail...
parties with him where they dr...
beer and wore their bathing su...

Filed With Liquor

On the night of July 30, she te...
...fied, after the second sailing tr...
she became "dizzy and nause...
after drinking "three or four
...ties of beer" and four "bour...
which she said Hattman Tat...
mitted ordering as "double dr...
without her knowledge.

She said he took her hom...
went into the small Rutledge
...ment with her.

"After you got inside. wh...
Mr. Hattman do to you?"
Milner, defense attorney, a...
heavily and her reply cam...
difficulty. Finally she told...
seduction.

"Did you consent to it?"
objection to this question ...
ruled).

She, "Wanted To Be...
was trying to plead wi...
leave. I was dizzy and
said I wanted to be alo...
very shortly and I don't...
anything after that.".

Drinking Is on the Increase

the duties of his station. An aching head and trembling limbs which are the inevitable effects of drinking disincline hands from work; hence begins sloth and that listlessness which end in idleness.

JOHN ADAMS
(1735–1826)

Adams fiercely resented the dram-shops and tippling houses of his day and

was grieved to the heart to see the number of idlers, sots and consumptives made in those infamous seminaries. They are become the eternal haunt of loose, disorderly people and in many cases the nurseries of our legislators. An artful man may, by gaining a little sway among the rabble of the town, multiply taverns and dram-shops and thereby secure the votes of taverner and retailer; the multiplication of taverns will make many who may be induced by flip and rum to vote for any man whatever.

You will find the house(s) full of people drinking drams, flip, toddy, carousing, swearing; but especially plotting with the landlord to get him at the next town meeting an election either for selectman or representative.

Scarcely anything that I have observed has a greater influence on the religion, morals, health, property, liberties and tranquillity of the world. The temper and the passions, the profaneness and brutal behavior inspired by the low sort of company that frequent such houses and by the liquors they drink there, are not very compatible with the pure and undefiled religion of Jesus—that religion whose first principle is to renounce all filthiness. The plentiful use of liquors begins with producing a strange confusion of mind, and

passions too violent for the government of reason; proceeds
to involve men in debts, and of consequence, in lying, cheating, stealing, and sometimes in greater crimes; and ends in
total and incurable dissolution of manners. Quarrels, duels,
riots, are daily hatching from eggs and spawns deposited in
the same nests. In short, these houses, like so many boxes
of Pandora, are sending forth each day innumerable plagues
that multiply fast enough to lay waste in a little while the
whole world.

A drunkard is the most selfish thing in the universe: he
has no sense of modesty, shame or disgrace; no sense of
duty, or sympathy of affection with his father or mother,
his brother or sister, his friend or neighbor, his wife or
children; no reverence for his God, no sense of futurity in
this world or the other. All is swallowed up in the mad,
selfish joy of the moment. Is it not humiliating that Ma-
hometans and Hindoos should put to shame the whole Christian world by their superior examples of temperance? And
is it not mortifying beyond all expression that we Americans
should exceed all others in this degrading, beastly vice of
intemperance?

(The Indian) Little Turtle petitioned me to prohibit rum
to be sold to his nation, because he said I had lost three
thousand of my Indian children in his nation in one year
by it.

THOMAS JEFFERSON
(1743–1826)

To the Indian, Brother Handsome Lake, 1802:

I am happy to hear that you have been so favored by
the Divine Spirit as to see the ruinous effects which the abuse
of spiritous liquors has produced upon your people. It has
weakened their bodies, enervated their minds, exposed them

to hunger, cold, nakedness, and poverty, kept them in perpetual broils, and reduced their population. And as it is the desire of your nation that no spirits should be sent among them, I am authorized by the great council of the United States to prohibit them.

—the whisky which kills one third of our citizens and ruins their families; destroying the fortunes, the bodies, the minds and morals of our citizens.

The drunkard, as much as the maniac, requires restrictive measures to save him from the fatal infatuation under which he is destroying his health, his morals, his family, and his usefulness to society. One powerful obstacle to his ruinous self-indulgence would be a price beyond his competence.
—To Samuel Smith, 1823.

The habit of using ardent spirits by men in office has occasioned more injury to the public and more trouble to me than all other sources. And were I to commence my administration again, the first question I would ask respecting a candidate to office would be, "Does he use ardent spirits?"
—From the Report of the American Temperance Society for 1833.

Of all calamities, this (intemperance) is the greatest.

JOHN QUINCY ADAMS
(1767–1848)

Speaking before the Norfolk County Temperance Society at Quincy, in 1842, Adams said:

The Society for the suppression of intemperance in the County of Norfolk is, in fact, a society to multiply the joys and diminish the sorrows of the whole people—a society to redeem them from vice and wretchedness.

At a meeting in his home town he declared:

I regard the temperance movement of the present day as one of the most remarkable phenomena of the human race, operating simultaneously in every part of the world for the reformation of a vice as infectious in its nature as smallpox or the plague, and combining all the ills of war, pestilence and famine. Among those who have fallen by intemperance are untold numbers who were respected for their talents and worth.

No party politics should be mingled with the subject, but moral reform should be the inscription on the temperance banner, which should be borne aloft, conquering and to conquer, from sea to sea, and to the ends of the earth.

JAMES BUCHANAN
(1791–1868)

In an address to the students of Franklin and Marshall College at Lancaster, Pa., Buchanan said that there was one habit which, if formed at college or in early youth, would cling to them through life and blight the fairest prospects. It would be better for that youth who contracted an appetite for strong drink that he were dead or had never been born; for when he saw a young man entering upon such a career, a fondness for liquor becoming with him a governing passion, he could see nothing before him but a life of sorrow and a dishonored grave. Many lads, he was aware, considered this practice a mark of smartness; but he regarded it as an offense that can not be pardoned.

ABRAHAM LINCOLN
(1809–1865)

In his *Abraham Lincoln* Lord Charnwood says: "It was a cock-fighting, whisky-drinking society in New Salem into which Lincoln at the age of twenty-two was launched. He managed to combine strict abstinence from liquor with keen participation in all its other diversions." In one of these, with a young man's eagerness to exhibit the physical strength for which he was famed, he hoisted a whisky barrel on to his knees in a squatting posture and drank from the bunghole; this was his single departure from his rule. But his own abstinence did not make him callous to the plight of his less temperate brothers. Once on a freezing night he picked out of a ditch near Gentryville, Indiana, a snoring drunkard, and bore him back to safety on his own strong shoulders.

On another occasion when he was attending court in Clinton, fifteen women had been indicted for sweeping down on a saloon and knocking in the heads of the barrels. Invited to say a few words in their behalf, Lincoln suggested that the indictment be changed to read, "The State of Illinois against Mr. Whisky." As the result of his defense the women were released.

There is a foreshadowing of the methods of the Alcoholics Anonymous in Lincoln's speech to the Washingtonian Temperance Society at Springfield, Feb. 22, 1842, a society largely composed of drunkards who had reformed:

Although the Temperance cause has been in progress near twenty years, it is apparent to all that it is just now being crowned with a degree of success hitherto unparalleled. This new and splendid success is doubtless owing to rational causes. The warfare heretofore waged against the demon intemperance has somehow or other been erroneous. The champions for the most part have been preachers, lawyers and hired agents. They are supposed to have no sympathy with those very persons whom it is their object to convince.

But when one who has long been a victim of intemperance bursts the fetters that have bound him, and appears before his neighbors "clothed and in his right mind," to tell of the miseries once endured, of his naked and starving children, new clad and fed comfortably; of a wife long weighed down with a broken heart, now restored to health, happiness and a renewed affection, there is a logic and an eloquence in it that few with human feeling can resist. The Washingtonians teach hope to all—despair to none. Drunken devils are cast out by legions; and their unfortunate victims are publishing to the ends of the earth how great things have been done for them.

Whether or not the world would be benefitted by a total and final banishment from it of all intoxicating drinks seems to me not now [any longer] an open question. Three fourths of mankind confess the affirmative with their tongues, and, I believe all the rest acknowledge it in their hearts. Ought any then to refuse their aid in doing what good the good of the whole demands?

The demon of intemperance ever seems to have delighted in sucking the blood of genius and generosity. He seems to have gone forth, like the Egyptian angel of death, commissioned to slay, if not the first, the fairest born of every family. Shall he now be arrested in his desolating career? In that arrest all can give aid; and who shall be excused that can and will not?

If the relative grandeur of revolutions shall be estimated by the amount of human misery they alleviate, and the small amount they inflict, then indeed will this be the grandest the world shall ever have seen. Of our political revolution of 1776 we are justly proud. In it was the germ which has vegetated, and still is to grow and expand into the universal liberty of mankind.

Turn now to the temperance revolution. In it we shall find a stronger bondage broken, a viler slavery manumitted, a greater tyrant deposed; in it, more of want supplied, more disease healed, more sorrow assuaged. By it no orphans starving, no widows weeping. By it, none wounded in feeling, none injured in interest. And when the victory shall be complete—when there shall be neither a slave nor a drunkard on earth—how proud the title of that land which may claim to be the birthplace of both those revolutions which have ended in that victory!

When, on May 19, 1860, a committee waited on Lincoln at his home in Springfield, Ill., to notify him of his nomination for President, "something to drink" was suggested. Lincoln said:

Gentlemen, we must pledge our mutual healths in the most healthy beverage which God has given to man. It is the only beverage I have ever used or allowed in my family and I cannot conscientiously depart from it on the present occasion—It is pure Adam's ale from the spring.

When members of the Temperance League presented to Lincoln a petition requesting that "every officer persisting in degrading himself, imperilling our cause, and ruining, by the wretched example of his drunkenness, the soldiers of his command, be dismissed from service," Lincoln said,

I think that the reasonable men of the world have long since agreed that intemperance is one of the greatest, if not the very greatest, of all evils among mankind:

and he promised to submit to the War Department their suggestions.

THE PRESIDENTS' DECLARATION

(A document circulated by Edward C. Delavan of New York from 1833 through the presidency of Andrew Johnson, to which he obtained the signatures of twelve of the Presidents:)

Being satisfied from observation and experience, as well as from medical testimony, that ardent spirit, as a drink, is not only needless, but hurtful, and that the entire disuse of it would tend to promote the health, the virtue, and the happiness of the community, we hereby express our conviction, that should the citizens of the United States, especially the young men, discontinue entirely the use of it, they would not only promote their personal benefit, but the good of our country and of the world.

James Madison	Zachary Taylor
John Quincy Adams	Millard Fillmore
Andrew Jackson	Franklin Pierce
M. Van Buren	James Buchanan
John Tyler	Abraham Lincoln
James K. Polk	Andrew Johnson

RUTHERFORD HAYES
(1822–1893)

Shortly after becoming President to the end of his life Hayes was a conscientious total abstainer. His great vigor, capacity for work and resiliency after periods of strain constitute the best possible argument for abstention from alcohol. He hoped that the pattern of abstinence set by the White House would be influential in discouraging the increasingly lavish use of intoxicants for social entertainment at the Capital and in the country at large.

Hearing that his successor Garfield intended to restore wine and liquor to the White House, he wrote in his diary, Jan. 16, 1881:

If General Garfield rejects the practice I have inaugurated, he will lose the confidence of thousands of good citizens and gain no strength in any quarter. His course will be taken as evidence that he lacks the grit to face fashionable ridicule. Nothing hurts a man more than a general belief that he lacks the courage of his convictions.

In his diary, Oct. 12, 1881, he wrote that the true methods of promoting temperance

are education, example, argument, and friendly and sympathetic persuasion. Legislation and political parties in the interest of temperance all aim at the liquor seller. They do not reach his customers. If he is a criminal, what is the man who tempts him? If there are no customers there will be no sellers.

In a letter to Mr. John Bruce of Glasgow:

Whatever may be true of other countries, I am satisfied that in America total abstinence from intoxicating liquors is the only safety. No doubt there are some men in the United States who can drink in moderation. But the majority will suffer serious injury and many will be ruined by the habit. No man can know beforehand that he can remain a moderate drinker. For Americans, with their nervous and excitable temperament, and with its tendency to excess, there is, in my opinion, no halfway house between total abstinence and danger. I have tried total abstinence. It has never interfered with my health or happiness or comfort, but has beyond question always promoted them.

WILLIAM McKINLEY

(1843-1901)

On July 10, 1874, McKinley made the following eloquent appeal to voters of Stark County, Ohio:

We need scarcely remind you that the liquor traffic which is sought to be legalized by the license section is one that deeply concerns not only the honor of this great state, but also the material, moral and social interests of all the people. There is not a home or hamlet in the state that is beyond its influence. Its evils are widespread and far-reaching.

Consider what the consequences will be if the license section carries. First we will legalize this great wrong. We will give the sanction of the Constitution and the laws of this great, free and intelligent state to this most degrading and ruinous of all human pursuits, so that men who are spreading ruin and death may say to all protestors: "Stand aside, my business has received the sacred sanction of the law, and is therefore legal and right." Second, by legalizing this traffic we agree to share with the liquor seller the responsibilities and evils of his business. Every man who votes for License becomes of necessity a partner to the liquor traffic and all its consequences.

THEODORE ROOSEVELT
(1858–1919)

As President of the New York Police Board Roosevelt began to enforce the Sunday-closing Law, which had become a dead letter, the saloons keeping wide open on Sundays under protection of the police who had been bribed. He succeeded in keeping them closed till his efforts were partly nullified by a court decision that the sale of food, even of one sandwich, was sufficient to legalize the accompanying sale of numberless drinks. Commenting upon the effects of the enforcement, Roosevelt wrote to Dr. Iglehart:

There could have been no more practical illustration of the hideous evil wrought by the liquor traffic than was afforded by the results of its stoppage for the few Sundays during which we were able to keep the saloons absolutely closed. During this period, the usual mass of individuals up in the courts on Monday morning, on charges of being drunk or disorderly or committing assaults, diminished by two thirds or over. The hospitals, such as Bellevue, showed a similar diminution of persons brought to them because of alcoholism and crimes due to drunkenness. Men who would otherwise have stayed in New York drinking, while their wives and children suffered in the heated tenement houses, took these same wives and children for a Sunday holiday in the country.

As was to be expected, the saloon men and gangsters, in a hearing before Mayor Strong, insolently demanded that their former privileges be restored. Commissioner Roosevelt replied:

Your Honor, these gentlemen have demanded that you require me to give a "liberal enforcement of the excise law," to enforce the law a "little bit," a little tiny bit. Your

Honor, I did not take oath to enforce the law a little tiny bit, and so long as I am head of the Police Department of the city I shall do all in my power to enforce the law honestly and fearlessly.

At another time he said:

The friends of the saloon keepers denounce their opponents for not treating the saloon business like any other. The best answer is that the business is not like any other business. The business tends to create criminality in the population at large and law-breaking among the saloon keepers themselves. When liquor men are allowed to do as they wish, they are sure to debauch, not only the body social, but the body politic also.

Canteens where intoxicants were sold had long been permitted in the army. After a protracted fight they were driven out. But the liquor forces threatened to restore them and Dr. Iglehart went to Washington to ask for assistance from President Roosevelt who assured him:

The removal of the drink from the army was a most fortunate thing for the men themselves and the nation they represent, and I promise you that so long as I am President, or so long as I shall have any influence whatever in the Republican party or in American politics, intoxicants shall never come back to the canteen.

After Congress had submitted the National Prohibition Amendment, Roosevelt wrote to Dr. Iglehart, Dec. 19, 1917:

I wish to congratulate you on what has happened in Congress and the success that is crowning your long fight against alcoholism. The American saloon has been one of the most mischievous elements in American social, political, and industrial life. No man has warred more valiantly against it than you have, and I am glad that it has been my privilege to stand with you in the contest.

In a letter to Clarence True Wilson, Dec., 1917:

When we must feed our army and help the armies of our allies, not a bushel of grain should be permitted to be made into intoxicating liquor. Neither the man in the army nor the man engaged in doing vital work for the army in connection with railroads, factories, mines and shipyards should be allowed to waste strength and health at this time.

WILLIAM HOWARD TAFT
(1857–1930)

Addressing the Sunday-schools of the United States at the time of a memorial service in honor of Lincoln at Springfield, Taft said:

My dear young Friends:

The excessive use of intoxicating liquor is the cause of a great deal of the poverty, degradation and crime of the world, and one who abstains from the use of liquor avoids a dangerous temptation. Abraham Lincoln showed that he believed this in writing out for his boy friends the pledge of total abstinence. Each person must determine for himself the course he will take in reference to his tastes and appetites, but those who exercise the self-restraint to avoid altogether the temptation of alcoholic liquor are on the safe and wiser side.

On another occasion he said:

He who drinks is deliberately disqualifying himself for advancement. Personally I refuse to take such a risk. I do not drink.

CHAPTER IV

THE DOCTORS TESTIFY

Sir William Osler, who has been called "the greatest physician in history," once said:

Alcohol does not make people do things better, it makes them less ashamed of doing them badly.

In *A Way of Life* he wrote:

In every large body of men a few are to be found whose incapacity for the day results from the morning clogging of nocturnally-flushed tissues. As moderation is very hard to reach, and as it has been abundantly shown that the best of mental and physical work may be done without alcohol in any form, the safest rule for the young man is abstinence.

George W. Webster, M.D., formerly Professor of Clinical Medicine, Northwestern University, has said:

To classify a sedative, injurious, habit-forming narcotic as a stimulant is a contradiction in terms. To prescribe alcohol at night as a sedative hypnotic and the next day as a stimulant in pneumonia, seems little less than ludicrous.

Richard M. Cabot, M.D.:

Scientific research revealed long ago that alcohol does not stimulate the heart under any conditions whatever. In view of this well-proved fact it follows as a corollary that all recommendations of alcohol as a means to support the hearts of elderly people are the merest rubbish. Alcohol never supported any heart, elderly or young, and never will. The same is true of alcohol for circulatory emergencies.

Sir Andrew Clark, M.D.:

Alcohol is a poison; so is strychnine; so is arsenic; so is opium; it ranks with these agents. Health is always in some way injured by it—benefitted never.

McCarthy and Douglass, in *Alcohol and Social Responsibility;* 1949:

A medical definition of poison characterizes it as "any substance . . . ingested, inhaled, or developed within the body which causes or may cause damage or disturbance of function." This definition is the broadest possible and permits the inclusion of innumerable substances not ordinarily thought of as poisonous. . . . Alcohol in small amounts may cause disturbance of function; dramatic functional disturbances follow the ingestion of large amounts.

Hermann Pfeiffer, M.D., University of Gratz, Austria:

To continually transport large quantities of liquids through the circulatory system is a great burden to it. And since liquors usually contain the narcotic poison, alcohol, there is a threefold effect produced. Eventually the heart undergoes degenerative changes as do the blood vessels, and finally the kidneys. It leaves the victim a wreck with no chance of a comeback.

Dr. Haven Emerson, editor of *Alcohol and Man,* in an article written for *The Christian Science Monitor:*

Alcohol is not a stimulant to be relied upon to improve the circulation, respiration or digestion. It has toxic or poisonous effects whenever used. These effects are chiefly if not exclusively due to action on the brain and other parts of the central nervous system and are mild or severe, acute or chronic according to the amount of alcohol consumed and the percentage circulating at any particular time in the blood.

The tendency of alcohol habitués is to increase the amounts they take, or the frequency of dosage, or to use the stronger, higher per cent alcoholic beverages in place of those of low content. The habitual user of alcohol who cannot voluntarily discontinue its use without suffering some considerable distress of body or mind, has become an addict and should put himself under treatment.

The effect of alcohol is mainly upon the behavior of the person, his emotions, his self-control, judgment, discretion. In chronic alcoholics the cells of the brain and other cells may undergo processes of degeneration. Alcohol dulls the higher faculties of the mind and the will before it has an appreciable effect upon locomotion or the use of the muscles of the body. Perception, association of ideas, memory, discrimination are all deteriorated by amounts of alcohol which do not create a condition of offense in the police or social sense.

Alcohol may decrease bodily resistance to infection and diminish the likelihood of recovery. The injured or infected alcoholic has more complications, a longer course to recovery, and a higher mortality from the common bacterial infections than if his body were free from alcohol.*

---

* For many years this warning was put into the hands of each post-operative surgical patient on leaving the Presbyterian Hospital in New York: "Avoid alcoholic drinks, with the idea that they are necessary to your health or that they will do you any good. Alcohol is a poison and you should know it."

Alcohol is a direct cause of various acute and chronic diseases and is a complicating and contributing factor in many others. From 10,000 to 12,000 patients suffering from acute or chronic forms of alcoholism are admitted for medical care each year to the psychiatric service of Bellevue Hospital in New York City.

The effects of alcohol upon the home are various, and all of them contribute to emotional instability, educational inadequacy, economic dependency, and personality problems, particularly among the children. Accidents in the home, in industry, on the farm, on the public highway are due, many of them directly, and still more of them indirectly, to the use of alcohol; not only to the point of obvious drunkenness, but when used in relatively moderate amounts.

From an article, *How Alcohol Affects the Brain,* also by Dr. Haven Emerson, while Commissioner of Health, New York City, and reprinted by *The Signal Press:*

Alcohol is a poison to all parts of the body, but the part which it can damage most quickly and to the greatest extent is the delicate and sensitive brain. The worst damage is done to the most delicate parts of the brain; and so it follows, that when a man takes a couple of drinks of strong liquor it quickly steals from him what is best in him; it reduces the force of highest brain control which he has developed through the ages, and which marks him out as different from the brute animals. Civilized man equals brute animals plus high brain development. Alcohol blots out the "high brain development" and leaves the brute animal.

Now of course, we don't mean to say that when a person takes a drink of anything containing alcohol he is reduced at once to a brute animal; but very few will dispute that a drunken person is not much better than a brute animal. Before he can take enough alcohol to kill his body, he has

4

had enough to paralyze his brain, especially the higher parts of his brain. Even a very little, though it does not show itself in drunkenness, has a changing effect on the brain. Too many people think that if they drink alcohol in moderation, such as three or four glasses of beer a day, they are not doing themselves any harm at all. Very many even think that they may safely drink as long as they stop before getting drunk. These are very dangerous and mistaken ideas to have.

Women and young persons sooner become victims of the brain-weakening effects of alcohol than men and older persons, because women and young persons have more sensitive nervous systems and brains. So it is clear that women and young persons should be particularly careful to steer clear of liquor.

A number of bookkeepers who have to deal with figures, which is the kind of work which requires a clear brain and can be easily compared from time to time, were given alcohol daily for two weeks in amounts that would equal what is contained in about four glasses of beer. At the end of two weeks their ability to add simple figures was reduced by 15 per cent.

In Sweden, soldiers were allowed moderate amounts of alcohol on certain days and none on others, and their ability to hit a target was tested. On the days when they got no alcohol they averaged 23 hits out of 30. On the days when they did get alcohol, they averaged only 3 hits out of 30 shots! These and many other similar tests clearly show how alcohol in moderation unsteadies the nerves and muddles the brain.

Finally, just one more warning. One of the most terrible effects of alcohol on the nervous system is delirium tremens—the "D.T.'s." Now, it is not necessary to drink oneself drunk to get the D.T.'s. Here is what a doctor who has handled an enormous number of alcoholic patients and who has made a lifelong study of their troubles, has to say: "Many men who have never been intoxicated but have for years steadily taken alcohol, will, after some severe accident, develop delirium tremens."

Remember: You don't need alcohol for health, you don't need it for strength, you don't need it for food, you don't need it for drink; it never does you any good. Then why drink?

The late Dr. Charles Mayo, of the famous Mayo Clinic, addressing a convention of boys:

You can get along with a wooden leg, but you can't get along with a wooden head. The physical value of man is not so much, it is the brain that counts.

A man who has to drag around a habit that is a danger and a menace to society ought to go off to the woods and live alone. We do not tolerate the obvious use of morphine or cocaine or opium, and we should not tolerate intoxicating liquor because, I tell you, these things are what break down the command of the individual over his own life and destiny. Keep yourselves free from all entangling habits.

Remember, it's the brain that counts!

Arthur E. Hollenbeck, M.D., in *Life and Health*, the National Health Journal:

Alcohol, as a beverage, has been used throughout the centuries, but there never has been such an intensive campaign to increase its consumption as there is at the present time. The liquor interests have employed the best talent in the advertising profession to popularize the use of alcoholic beverages. Our popular magazines are filled with beautiful advertisements to make the use of alcoholic drinks attractive. The billboards in our cities and along our highways are plastered with liquor advertisements placed there at enormous expense for but one purpose—to educate the youth that it is the smart thing to use alcoholic beverages.

There is a movement under way to prove and to advertise as a fact that alcohol is food. If a food is considered to be any substance which can be oxidized or burned in the body, alcohol is a food. But there are innumerable poisons which can be oxidized in the body even more readily than alcohol, yet there is little interest in trying to classify them as foods.* The whole idea is to deceive, by attempting to educate the younger generation into believing that alcohol is actually beneficial to the body rather than injurious.

Why all this change in attitude toward the liquor traffic in recent years? Has the effect of alcohol changed in modern times, or is there simply a well-organized plan to fill the coffers of the liquor traffic at the expense and degradation of its patrons?

The man who drinks, even in moderation, destroys safeguards to health in heated summer weather. The records of various hospitals showed that 98 per cent of the cases of heat prostration treated in those institutions were due to habitual indulgence in alcoholic drinks, and, of these, 44 per cent died.† One prominent physician has stated that if alcohol were taken out of the world, the number of hospital cases would be reduced by half.

The keen competition of modern business and the increase of powerful, high-speed machinery demand of man the highest possible degree of efficiency. On account of their

---

* Alcohol differs from food in that, lacking vitamins, it never rebuilds body tissue, though it does temporarily supply energy in the form of calories. The U. S. Brewers' *Year Book* for 1913 states: "Chemists and brewers admit that practically the food value of alcohol and even of beer is inconsiderable. The quantity necessary to nourish the system would be so large as to act as a poison."

† Similarly in extreme cold, as polar explorers know, even one dose of alcohol is dangerous as causing dissipation of body heat from the flushed surface, and so lowering the actual temperature of the body and rendering it less capable of enduring zero weather.

well-known impaired reliability and lessened efficiency, habitual users of alcohol are crowded out of many of the higher fields of employment.

Alcohol is a direct poison to the nervous system and one of the most common causes of mental disease. It is listed as second only to heredity as the cause of insanity. Since it is physiologically a poison and not a food, essentially a drug and not a drink, the effects of its ingestion are directly to produce degeneration of nearly all the bodily tissues, and indirectly to increase the liability to many diseases by lessening the systemic powers of resistance, thus favoring fatality from such diseases.

The symptoms of alcoholic poisoning develop very gradually and are usually marked for some time by the deceptive sensations of stimulation, warmth, and well-being. Impairment of digestion is early noted. A coated tongue, foul breath, vomiting before meals, and gastric distress after eating; constipation alternating with diarrhea are common. Muscular tremors gradually develop, insomnia, mental impairment and blunting of the moral senses come on. In this distress the inebriate seeks to relieve himself by taking more alcohol, only to find, on awakening from the stupor, that body, intellect, will, and emotion are still more depraved. As conscience and restraint are paralyzed, it is little wonder that among imbibers sexual promiscuity is frequent. Public health officials claim that venereal diseases have increased 20 per cent since the repeal of Prohibition.

Dr. C. Kellick Millard:

Speaking as a Medical Officer of Health, I can say that if I were given the choice of abolition, on the one hand, of the drink evil, and on the other, of all the other preventable influences adversely affecting the public health on which medical officers are at present concentrating their efforts, I would choose unhesitatingly the abolition of drink, as being greater by far than all the others combined.

Weekly *Bulletin* of the New York City Dept. of Health, Feb. 19, 1916.

The discontinuance of the use of alcohol will mark a greater advance in public health protection than anything since the application of our knowledge of the bacterial origin of disease.

The prevailing idea that beer is a comparatively harmless drink, containing as it does less alcohol than other liquor, is stoutly refuted by medical authorities. The fact that it is usually absorbed in much greater quantities about equalizes its destructiveness.

At the International Congress against Alcoholism in Vienna, it was reported that of 1525 alcoholics studied, 825 had drunk only beer; of these, 483 took over five quarts a day each, while of the whisky drinkers, 243 took daily over a half-pint each. Thus each beer drinker got five ounces of alcohol daily compared with the whisky drinkers' four ounces of alcohol. Of these beer drinkers, twenty-nine died of delirium tremens.

In one place investigated at least 80 per cent of the cases were beer topers. In another, 90 per cent were either beer or wine drinkers. Says Dr. Eugene Lyman Fisk of the Life Extension Institute, "Alcohol is alcohol, either in whisky or beer. It is nonsense to claim that beer is a hygienic drink."

Babe Ruth was once asked to hold a bottle of beer while being photographed. "No," said he, "I have autographed too many baseballs for the boys of America to think of helping to advertise the sale of beer."

Said Matt Mann, Swimming Coach, University of Michigan:

The big purpose of athletics is to build better men, both morally and physically. Alcohol in any form can only tear down, so that there is absolutely no place in athletics for alcoholic poison.

George Beurling, Canada's outstanding flying ace in the last war, is the only ace ever to have received four decorations at one presentation. He is a total abstainer from alcohol and tobacco. In a letter to his mother he once said:

In this game, split seconds count, and if it hadn't been for your training, I probably wouldn't be here. Smoking and drinking slow up your mind, and reactions are bound to be slower.

Dr. J. M. T. Finney, the celebrated Baltimore surgeon, related this episode of himself when a young medical student:

Just before the Medical School opened at the beginning of my third year, I came down with an attack of typhoid fever. When I began to get better I developed an enormous craving for food, but the only thing allowed typhoid convalescents in those days was milk and whisky. I despised the milk and loved the whisky, so much so that I found myself impatiently watching the clock for the time the next drink of whisky was due. One day while doing this, the thought occurred to me, "What does all this mean, this tremendous interest and craving for whisky?" I reached the conclusion that so far as I was concerned, it was time to stop. . . . That was my last drink. If one wants a quick stimulant, a non-habit-forming and equally effective substitute, may readily be found. This is a matter in which a doctor bears to his patients a definite responsibility which cannot lightly be disregarded.*

The late Dr. Howard Kelly, of Johns Hopkins Medical School said:

There is no single disease in the world of which alcohol is the cure. Since alcohol cures no disease, it is not a medicine.† It creates only an illusion of vigor that does not exist. Its high potency as a dangerous drug is a million times more hurtful than any conceivable accruing advantage.

---

* From *A Surgeon's Life,* by J. M. T. Finney. Copyright, 1940, by J. M. T. Finney. Courtesy of G. M. Putnam's Sons.

† Whisky is no longer listed in the United States Pharmacopœia, the standard book of authority on drugs and medicines.

Chapter V

THE MODERATE DRINKER HAS HIS SAY AND IS ANSWERED

"Naturally I look with horror on any excessive indulgence in drink, but beer, wine, cocktails and so forth taken in moderation are aids, necessities even, to gracious living. They are social lubricators, help to liven up a party. All of our set serve them as a matter of course, and you have to do what everybody else is doing. Why, even my doctor told me once that it wasn't a bad thing to take a cocktail to freshen one up before dinner. Drinking in moderation won't hurt you in the least.

"I heard what your doctors said just now about how liquor affects the brain, the physiological changes it causes; and 'If you drink, don't drive, if you drive, don't drink' has become a radio commonplace around the holidays;—of course I shouldn't want my chauffeur to drink, or the engineer of the Colonial Express, or a trained nurse or servants and all such people—it would be dangerous or at least affect their efficiency. But it's absurd to say that those physiological laws apply to us;—if they do, they ought to be changed!

"Why, the other day when I left a friend's house after taking several martinis, I never felt more fit in my life. I was in high spirits as I sailed off in the brand-new Buick, and found that I was driving more cleverly than usual and so could afford to take some risks. Everything was fine until the crash. The trouble was with the lights—they both looked grayish; and I didn't see the other fellow till he was right on me. It's a terrible shame about the new Buick—one side smashed. And of course I was horribly distressed about the little child that was killed and have done what I could to make amends to the parents. But it was a good thing I was driving, or the accident might have been worse than it was.

"Well, our grandfathers always had wine on the table, and most of the smart people we know are using it more and more. And anyway, things were a great deal worse when we had Prohibition,—there was more drinking and bootlegging then than now.

"Drinking gives one a chance to exercise self-control. One should learn to drink like a gentleman, and if one can't, why it's just too bad. I see no reason why I should give up the pleasure of drinking in a moderate way with my friends just because the other fellow doesn't know when to stop. I can't undertake to be my brother's keeper!"

The Moderate Drinker Answered

You intimate that one can be moderate if one wishes and that drinking affords a chance to exercise self-control. So does opium; but that is no reason for allowing this dangerous drug to be accessible to all. No one starts drinking with the intention of becoming an alcoholic; but it is estimated that one out of every sixteen who drink at all becomes an alcoholic by middle life, and there is no possible way, doctors assert, of telling beforehand which drinkers will develop addiction,—it may be you, or the one to whom you have just offered that drink! There are three to four million alcoholics in the United States today, some 750,000 of them women, and the number is constantly on the increase.

As for the doctor who told you it would do you no harm to take a cocktail before dinner,—he was a drinker himself, and was unconsciously trying to reinforce his own position. (It has been stated that fifty per cent of doctors over fifty years of age are addicts to either drugs or drink.) But Dr. Haven Emerson, former Commissioner of Health, New York City, has said: "Of all physiologically undesirable habits in the use of alcohol, the cocktail before meals in the homes of fashion and the whiskey before breakfast in the homes of alcohol addicts are the worst in their immediate and subsequent effect upon the health of the individual." This is because the alcohol in those drinks, not being partly absorbed by any food in the stomach, can then act more strongly upon the system.

The moderate drinker is accountable not only for his own possible excesses, but for those of the persons to whom he passes drinks. Of course there are many who manage to adhere to moderation all through life; unfortunately the finer such persons are, the more controlled, the more sanction does their example lend to the practice of social drinking. The beginner can quote them with the greater gusto as a precedent for his beginning to drink, and the immoderate drinker as an excuse for his inordinate use of the bottle.

General Lew Wallace was a commanding figure in his small home town in Indiana. With a distinguished war-record behind him, author, artist, lawyer as well, he used to look every inch the General as, brisk and erect, he walked down the street every afternoon for his single drink with his old cronies at the bar. One day, however, he found none of his friends at the rendez-vous, and, seeing the village toper in a corner of the room, called "Come over here, Charley, and have a drink with me!" The old fellow crossed the room and said, "General, I'll not drink with you. There's nobody in this town that drinks because old Charley drinks; but there's many a young fellow who begins to drink because he sees the General doing it. No, I'll not drink with you!"

Life insurance companies have found that the "moderate drinkers" have a life-expectancy forty per cent less than abstainers; English and Australian companies show a mortality rate for ordinary policy-holders fifty per cent greater than for total abstainers. The New England Mutual, in the period 1844-1905, taking

CONVICTED
TAL CRASH

Of Manslaughter In ighway Deaths

pants of an automobile headon into a station killing four members of a unty farm family, were manslaughter yester- Circuit Court for anty.

of the youthful occu- station wagon wer eath following the col 17 on Route 40 nea ship, Howard county tims Of Crash

ecution contended that of the other vehicle ntoxicated man to drive

FIC TOLL
CHES 6,208

5,880 Hurt In State
n 9 Months May 31 1946

asualties in Maryland day row stand at more per cent of the total men killed and wounded the European Theater ns in World War II.

Traffic Safety Commis- ic's show 328 motorists trians were killed in dents in the State from 1 through April 30. and

OS KILL
HILDREN;
VER HELD

llege Students usly Hurt In hird Crash 1949

dren were killed, one by iver, police said, and six brothers from Washing- d serious injuries in affic accidents in or near yesterday.

-old motorist, arrested fatalities, was charged ess driving, speeding, le drunk, failing to stop il accident and causing an East Baltimore

Movies Will Be Made Of Drunken Drivers

Washington, June 19 (AP)—Wash- ington's drunken drivers are going to be starred in the movies—pro- vided they get themselves arrested in the daytime.

And if police have their way, there won't be any question about when a driver is "staggering drunk."

Armed with a 16 millimeter mo- tion picture camera, police plan to rush to the scene of drunken driv- ing arrests to snap pictures of the

Mauck was driving at the time of the mishap. Mauck told Judge James Clark he had been drinking and did not know who was at the wheel.

Car Driver Charged After Boy Is Injured

A 14-year-old boy was struck by an automobile last night and police charged the motorist with driving while under the influence of alcohol and reckless driving.

Admitted to City Hospitals, Lindy Redding, of Fairfield, Pa., was be- ing operated on early this morning for command

Murder Without Malice Laid To Texas Judge

Houston, Texas, Nov. 24 (AP)— Judge Allie Peyton of County Court at Law No 2 went to trial to- day in District Judge Langston King's court here on an indictment charging murder without malice.

The 39-year-old jurist, charged in an indictment with being intoxi- cated when his car struck and fatally injured George McFarlin.

CAR HITS 3 WOMEN;
2 HURT CRITICALLY

morn. Sun, Jan. 17 '48

Driver Is Charged With Being Under Influence Of Liquor

Two young women were criti- cally injured and a third sustained minor injuries last night when they were struck by an automobile whose driver was charged by police with driving while under the influence of liquor.

Traffic Deaths Record Seen In West Virginia

morn. Sun Dec 22 '48

Charleston, W.Va., Dec. 21 (AP)— With ten days still remaining in 1948, highway traffic deaths in the State already have equaled those for all of last year.

The latest death reported to the State police accident prevention bureau brought the month's total to 24 and the year's to 388.

ARRESTED ON DRUNK CHARGE—Robert Walker, Hollywood actor, arrested in Los Angeles yesterday on drunk charge snaps his fingers as he sits in the police station afterward

Detroit Judge Free On Drinking Charge

Detroit, Nov. 24 (AP) — Circuit Judge George B. Murphy, arrested Saturday night on a drunken-driv- ing charge, was free today, pending trial January 22 in Traffic Court.

The Harvard-educated judge stood mute to the charge today, and a plea of innocent was ordered entered for him. Traffic Judge John D. Watts released him without bond.

"It was just the aftermath of the Yale-Harvard game," police quoted Judge Murphy as saying. They said he admitted having "about four highballs" while listening to a broadcast of the game at a club.

Motormen Under Drunk-Driver Law

[Annapolis Bureau of The Sun] Annapolis, Feb. 14 — Streetcar operators today were made liable to the laws of Maryland relating to driving vehicles while under the influence of intoxicating beverages or drugs.

The law is the result of an arrest of a motorman for "drunken driv- ing" of a trolley in Baltimore last year. The case was thrown out of court when the magistrate was un- able to find any statute to cover the charge of operating a streetcar while intoxicated.

The law was one of 25 signed to-

AUTO DRIVERS
WARNED ABOUT
DRUNKENNESS

Atkinson And Other Police Officials Give Advice About Parties

The Sun Dec 30, 1946

Augmented forces of city, county and State police will be detailed on New Year's Eve, in an effort by authorities to prevent holiday ac- cidents such as occurred at Christ- mas, when nine persons died in Maryland traffic mishaps.

Police officials yesterday warned motorists particularly against reck- less and drunken driving.

Hamilton R. Atkinson, Baltimore police commissioner, said:

"All city police will be instructed to be on the lookout for obviously inebriated persons who attempt to drive their cars."

"Will Receive No Mercy"

Col. Beverly Ober, superintend- ent of the State police, warned that "drunken drivers will receive no mercy from us."

Urging especial care by motorist during the holiday, the colonel added:

"Ninety per cent of reckless dri ing has its source in the use alcohol. State troopers—althou

'DRUNK 25 YEARS,'
FILM STAR QUOTE

Robert Walker Fined $50, G Driver Of His Car $150

Los Angeles, Oct. 22 (AP)—Rob Walker, of the films, pleaded gu today to being drunk and disorde and paid a $50 fine in Police Co

Walker's girl friend of last ni Thelma Patricia Byrnes, 22, was piloting the actor's 1949 was fined $150 when she guilty to drunken driving. She an alternative to 30 days in

"Wanted To Fight 5 Officers"

A radio officer who made arrest, L. L. Brown, said the s 000-a-year actor resisted booked as "drunk, noisy, loud boisterous," and that force ha be used to subdue him.

"Walker became belligeren wanted to fight five officers at station." Brown said of the 6- 145-pound Walker.

Walker's first wife was Jen Jones, his second Barbara daughter of John Ford, the director. Barbara's suit for div is pending.

"Lady Isn't Drunk," He Sa "Why. I've been drunk fo years," Lieut. E. C. Wiener qu

TOLL OF HOLIDAY DEATHS
MOUNTS TO 218, WITH 183
DYING IN TRAFFIC MISHAPS

morn. Sun

California's List Of 50 Accident Victims Highest In Nation; Safety Council Had Estimated 150 Would Be Killed In 2-Day Period

Eight killed, 18 hurt in holiday accidents in Maryland....Page 20

Chicago, Dec. 25 (AP)—The holiday death toll through- out the nation since 6 P.M. Christmas Eve mounted to 218 tonight, including 183 traffic deaths, 50 of them in California

the mortality among total abstainers to be 100, found
that of infrequent users to be 122, of temperate users,
142, of persons describing themselves as "moderate
users," 212.

One company reports that since 1932 rejections for
heavy alcoholic indulgence increased 183 per cent
among people under thirty! The moderate daily
drinker does more harm to his physique than does the
occasional heavy drinker who goes on a bat every
month or so and must take several days to get the alcohol out of his system. The other's system is daily taxed
to expel the poison from his blood. No, a bad thing is
never desirable, even in moderation. We should think
little of one who indulged moderately in thieving, lying,
or arsenic.

Most of the forty per cent or more of highway accidents which are due to drink are caused by the moderate drinker, .1 and .2 per cent of alcohol in the blood
being sufficient to narrow and blur the vision, obscure
the difference between the red and green lights, increase recklessness, impair judgment and self-control,
and seriously slow up the reactions in an emergency.
The National Safety Council states that the quantity
contained in an ounce of whisky or a bottle of beer
is sufficient to lower the ability of driver or pedestrian
to use the street safely. This relatively moderate amount
of alcohol affects precisely those nerve-muscle responses
which are most essential for safe driving; the effects
may appear a few minutes after drinking and continue
for five or more hours thereafter. One of the most

serious effects is that objects appear dimmer and consequently farther away than they are. Dr. Samuel R. Gerber, the coroner of Cuyahoga County, Ohio, in a ten year study conducted at Cleveland, found that the alcohol incidence for automobile fatalities during that time reached more than fifty per. cent, and that the greatest number of killers at the wheel were "moderate" drinkers. If you are a "moderate" user, then, you will be safest off the road!

You think you must drink because "everybody else is doing it," because it is "the adult thing to do." You are afraid of being a kill-joy, of being "different," of appearing unsophisticated. But by yielding to a custom you know to be unscientific, stupid and dangerous, you are declaring in the most pronounced fashion your lack of maturity and intelligence; you renounce your liberty of action, make it more difficult for others to act with independence, and dull your perceptions and inhibitions, so that while under the influence of alcohol you may commit indiscretions, even crimes, that later you have no recollection of and would abhor when entirely sober. The illusion cherished by drinkers that they are wittier after drinking results from their lowered standards and lack of discrimination at the time: to the sober onlooker they are merely noisier and more talkative, often vulgar. "When I am having a good time I want to know it," says Lady Astor; "I don't want my brain muddled with alcohol."

How pathetically absurd that a common Monday morning greeting should consist in cheap wisecracks turning upon the dissipation of the day before,—the

Sunday set apart by common consent of mankind for the refreshment and reinforcement of body, mind and soul; and that the student, "socialite," stenographer and clerk who cannot boast a handsome blue-Monday hangover should feel apologetic and convicted of being a failure with their kind! Dr. Robert V. Seliger, after many years of experience in the treatment of alcoholics, has said he is convinced that heavy social drinkers, numbering into the millions, actually cause more trouble as a group than do the alcoholics.

Once convinced of the insanity of absorbing daily an amount, however little, of poison into one's system, and of offering it to one's friends, a sturdy man or woman can quite enjoy swimming against the tide, and, if dynamic enough, seeing it gradually turn and flow the other way. Says Thoreau, "The faintest assured objection which one healthy man feels will at length prevail over the arguments and customs of mankind."

> One all against the world,
> One undismayed, intact.
> Shame when my flag is furled,
> Death when I break my pact!
> (E. Preston Dorgan)

Emily Dickinson had a way of compressing great things in little compass; we can't help being braced by this:

> On a columnar self
> How ample to rely;
> In tumult or extremity
> How good the certainty
> That lever cannot pry,
> And wedge cannot divide

Conviction, that granitic base,
Though none be on our side.

Suffice us for a crowd,
Ourselves—and rectitude—
And that Companion not far off
From furthest good man—
God.*

"God and one constitute a majority." The decision made once for all to exercise our mature judgment in the matter, and to stand on our own feet rather than float with the tide, each of us might well win over some other one of our set, and so the circle of the sane would constantly enlarge.

"Our grandfathers drank," it is true; and our great grandfathers had slaves; but the slave-holder is gone, and the despot Drink who holds in subjection slaves more abject than those must go too. Our grandfather did not live in a machine age; if he chanced to be a bit tipsy, he was not necessarily a menace, a casualty or a murderer on the highway; old Dobbin would take over and bring him safely home. Science has made important advances since Grandfather's day. He thought alcohol a stimulant; but its poisonous and depressant properties are now fully known; to absorb them is insane.

As to the amount of drinking and bootlegging during Prohibition compared with that today, the moderate drinker indulges in wishful thinking and has not troubled to ascertain the facts. No welfare or temperance worker wished the repeal of Prohibition, as they

---

* From *Poems* by Emily Dickinson, by permission of Little, Brown & Co.

would have had they then found conditions worse. Drinking has been heavily on the increase. The per capita consumption in the United States rose from 1.69 gallons a year in 1933, the last year of Prohibition, to 8.39 gallons in 1934 and 20.73 gallons in 1945. That there was then an increase of drinking in a very few of the larger eastern colleges is true. However, to a questionnaire sent by Dr. F. G. Southworth to the deans of 486 American colleges during Prohibition, asking "Has drinking increased among your students since Federal Prohibition came into effect?" the tenor of 309 of the replies was overwhelmingly to the effect that there had been a marked decrease in drinking. The thirteen which either reported or implied an increase gave as contributory causes the laxity of manners and morals incident upon the Great War and the fact that many young men had contracted drinking habits while in Europe.

Federal expense for curtailing of bootlegging in 1948 was more than $2,000,000 in excess of what it was at its highest during Prohibition. In Alabama the number of law enforcement agents employed to catch moonshiners had to be increased from thirty in 1937 to ninety in 1944. In the Fifth Federal District (Maryland, Virginia, West Virginia, North Carolina and District of Columbia), 182 stills were seized in January and February of 1943, 228 stills in the same months in 1944, 386 in January and February of 1945. 6053 stills were seized in the United States in 1947, 6757 in 1948.

Finally, the moderate drinker who will not sacrifice a passing pleasure for his brother's good forgets per-

5

haps that the man who first indignantly asked "Am I
my brother's keeper?" had every reason for wishing
to disclaim responsibility in the matter; for Cain had
just slain his brother and naturally resented any inquiry
about him. But St. Paul takes a different view: "Let
no man put a stumbling-block or an occasion to fall in
his brother's way. It is good not to drink wine or do
anything that makes your brother stumble. We that
are strong ought to bear the infirmities of the weak and
not to please ourselves." The inconsistency of the moderate drinker lies in his secret wish that his young
people should not incur the dangers of drink though he
is himself unwilling to forego its delights,—the only
argument that would have any weight with them.

In *Alcoholics Anonymous,* an interesting and sug-
gestive book for drinkers and non-drinkers alike, the
idea is stressed that self-will and self-centeredness are
at the root of the alcoholic's troubles, selflessness and
renewed contact with God the way back to life. The
same applies to us all, though we may never have fallen
prey to their particular enemy. Must we undergo their
agonies in order to realize that living for our own
selfish pleasure is the shortest road to ruin, and that
taking thought for others is the way to Life itself? The
essential part of the alcoholic's cure is the passing on
to others in desperate need what has been of help to
him. It is the central secret of life actually put into
effect.

The weak point of their ministrations is that they
practice only cure, not prevention of alcoholics, who,

with the present accessibility of alcohol, are being manufactured faster than they can possibly be cured. They even seem to take pride in the growing numbers of alcoholics who attend their meetings and in the fact that they can and do mix and pass drinks to their friends. If, on the contrary, they would unite with all other "men of goodwill" in advocating abstinence for all, their association might fade away as quickly as it came into prominence to meet the need occasioned by Repeal. As it is, they play into the hands of the liquor interests and are encouraged by them because they often convert to respectability the alcoholics who bring the trade into disrepute, but take no stand against the use of alcohol by the average drinker from whose ranks are recruited new legions of inebriates.

The moderate drinker may be moderate, for a time at least, but he is many; and the aggregated millions of drinks that he consumes supply the main support of those modern tyrants, the distilleries. He is, says Dr. Earl F. Zeigler, "the best advertiser that the liquor industry has." It follows that drinking in moderation, even if it were possible for the majority of mankind, is not the solution of the liquor problem; it is the main cause of that problem. The moderate drinker is always a candidate for alcoholism, the total abstainer never. If the sagacious old Dr. Samuel Johnson could say, "Abstinence is as easy to me as temperance would be difficult," no doubt our wisest course will be to follow suit.

CHAPTER VI

THE WOMAN DRINKER

Ah, wasteful woman! She who may
*   On her sweet self set her own price,*
Knowing man cannot choose but pay,
*   How she has cheapened Paradise!*
How given for naught her priceless gift,
*   How spoiled the bread and spilled the wine,*
Which spent with due respective thrift,
*   Had made brutes men and men divine!*
                    —Coventry Patmore.

Several years ago the Baltimore *Sun* carried an item about a woman arrested for drunken disorderliness on the street. Her twelve-year old son happening to pass under the window behind whose bars she was confined, she hailed him and told him of her plight. He pleaded with the magistrate so eloquently,—"She is an elegant lady when she is not drunk," that, moved by the upright manliness of the little fellow, the magistrate gave her her release pending her good conduct.

60

However, in spite of this reprieve, in three weeks she had to be taken up again for the same offence.

Another item described a family of four children from six years of age down, reported to the police by a commiserating neighbor. The officers found the children half-clothed and huddled together for warmth in a frigid room where the only article of food or drink was a half-emptied whisky bottle. The little girl of six was drunk, two of the younger children were in convulsions. The mother was discovered drinking in a near-by tavern. How far fallen is this guardian of the home from Wordsworth's

—perfect Woman, nobly planned,
To warn, to comfort, and command;
. . . . a Spirit, bright
With something of an angel light!

In this case it would never occur to us to blame the six-year old child for her drunken excess rather than the mother who was responsible for bringing it about; yet how few of us realize that the smiling hostess offering cocktails to her guests, many of whom find it difficult to refuse them, and a few of them impossible, perhaps, to do so, partakes of that mother's guilt in that she may be starting or confirming some man or woman in a career of alcoholism? We should not forget that practically all alcoholics begin their experience with alcohol in response to social pressure, in this way learning the temporary release from inhibitions and worry which it brings, and so the more readily resorting to it regularly, especially in times of stress and difficulty.

Few of us realize either how, since the beginning of the first World War, when a large number of potential drinkers were overseas, the women and young people of the country have been exploited by the brewery and distillery industries. At their convention in Chicago in 1935, among other promotional objectives were listed: "Teach American women to drink. Invite and welcome them to your bars and taprooms. We need to understand the habits of women and the younger generation. Train your publicity to catch the eye and develop the interest of the younger generation. Make youth liquor conscious. Make it smart to drink wine."

As the result of this policy, vast and glamorous advertising campaigns were launched, Seagram's alone spending six million dollars in one year; the hope being not only to double the consumption of liquor, but to double also the political power of the producers. Hitherto they had been used to buy legislation; by educating women to become steady drinkers, they could now buy the *votes* of the poor victims themselves.

Another desperate move adopted by the liquor industry was the appointment of a woman magazine writer and popular lecturer on woman's social sphere as director of the Women's Division of the Allied Liquor Industries, the purpose being to enlist the active support of women against the drys and all temperance organizations.

Due to the success of this campaign, as well as to the greater equality in recent years between men and women, and the change in the social attitude towards the drinking and smoking of women, the ratio of women alcoholics to men in the United States has increased from one to every five male alcoholics prior to 1931, to one to every two or three males now, until there are an estimated 750,000 women alcoholics, and the psychiatric wards of the country abound with female nicotine wrecks. For this social attitude we are each and all responsible, but especially the women, who, more than men, are creators of the social pattern.

Women are, perhaps, more sensitive to social pressure than men, and, being more nervously organized, deteriorate more quickly from drink. Though a bloated appearance, premature aging, tremor of the hands and sluggishness of mind often accompany habital drinking, the immediate effect upon the behavior is still more disastrous. The most correct society matron after drinking can become entirely careless of appearance, vulgar and profane in speech and utterly indecorous in her conduct toward the other sex. A typical example of this is the patient in the private sanitarium who has to be avoided by the doctors during the first twenty-four hours of her intoxication because, while in that state, she insists upon throwing her arms around their necks and hugging them.

Children of drinking mothers are born with less vigor than others and with every promise of maladjustment and delinquency resulting from the lack of faithful care and satisfying home life. For the mother is *par excellence* the maker of man,—a broken home is a pitiful environment for growing boys and girls. The Juvenile Protective Association of Chicago finds that "the excessive use of liquor has become an increasingly significant factor in child delinquency, divorce and separations."

It is interesting to note that in a recent survey of the drinking habits of 336 college girls it was found that while only forty-five of them were non-drinkers, and frequency of drinking was closely related to frequency of "dating," a larger proportion of non-drinkers than drinkers had chances for "going steady" or becoming engaged. It is certain that the promising young man of today as of all other days prefers as the mother of his children the girl who does not drink.

It will be objected perhaps by well-to-do women drinkers that the stories told at the beginning of this chapter do not in any way apply to them,—they are not arrested for drunkenness on the street, nor do they leave their children half-clothed and without attendance. But how infinitely sadder it is when privileged women in the privacy of their well-padded homes indulge in drink to a point that entirely unfits them for any real motherhood of their children, or leadership in the home and community! Because they are smuggled off to sanitaria when they become unbearable, instead of to prison, their disgrace is no less. They seem utterly to forget that *noblesse oblige*.

According to the fingerprint records of the FBI over seventeen times as many women were arrested in the United States in 1948 as in 1932 for driving while intoxicated, and 16,272 were arrested and fingerprinted for intoxication as against 694 in the eleven months of

"The Absinthe Drinker" from the painting by Picasso

1932 for which reports were received. 2673 women in the city of Washington alone were arrested for drunkenness in the year ending June 30, 1945; and from 1941 to 1945 arrests there of girls under twenty-one increased 130 per cent. In an address at Miami Beach in December, 1945, Mr. J. Edgar Hoover, Director of the FBI, said: "The arrests of girls under 18 years of age have increased 198% since the last peacetime year of 1939."

It has become unfortunately common too for trained nurses to drink. In this they are as much more guilty than was the renowned Sairey Gamp with her tea-pot full of spirits as they are more fully informed than she of the poisonous nature of alcohol and of the state of irresponsibility it brings about.

On page 76 of this book are given the findings of Prof. Peloman on the careers of all the known descendants of a drinking woman living about 1760. Out of the 709, 569 were either illegitimate, beggars, supported by their townships, prostitutes or criminals.

In comparison with the mother of this "beautiful family," let us consider the wife of President Hayes. With her husband, Mrs. Hayes set the fashion of serving no alcoholic drinks during their incumbency in the White House. As a result of this courageous defiance of the usual custom, a portrait of Mrs. Hayes was presented to the nation and hung in the White House; an address of commendation was sent to her bearing the autographs of hundreds of men and women, some of the most eminent and influential in the country, all testifying to the appreciation and admiration of their authors. Oliver Wendell Holmes, George W. Cable and J. T. Trowbridge were among the writers of verses; Elizabeth Stuart Phelps sent her greetings to one "who has the dignity, courage and fidelity of her convictions." Thomas Wentworth Higginson called "the White House whiter and purer because Mrs. Hayes became its mistress." Charles Dudley Warner wrote, "A good deed outlasts official position."

Edward Eggleston, "To perform one's function with fidelity and simplicity is to be both hero and saint."

Frederick Douglass, the Negro leader, "The fragrance of her goodness will linger forever about the Executive Mansion."

Josiah G. Holland, "Woman alone can make wine-drinking unfashionable, and heal the nation of its curse."

Whittier,

>Her presence lends its warmth and health
>>To all who come before it;
>If woman lost us Eden, such
>>As she alone restore it.

Longfellow,

>Whene'er a noble deed is wrought,
>Whene'er is spoken a noble thought,
>Our hearts in glad surprise
>To higher levels rise.

It will be remembered that Mrs. Cleveland, perhaps the most popular and charming of all the First Ladies of the land, was a total abstainer too; and Mrs. McKinley throughout life was an ardent advocate of temperance, one of the original band of Crusaders in Canton, Ohio.

Most ardent of all was that "uncrowned queen of American democracy," Frances E. Willard (1839-1898), who, ten years before the title was applied to Jane Addams, was called "the best-loved woman in America." At her fifty-fifth birthday celebration the President of the Illinois Federation of Labor paid "the tribute of honor and love to the woman who struck from millions the shackles forged by rum;" and the official publication of the Knights of Labor declared that no woman in America had done more or better work in the reform field, not only in the cause of temperance, but in the elevation of mankind in every way." At her funeral some thirty thousand men, women and children braved a heavy storm to stand in line for hours for the chance to look once more upon her face.

In the Chicago of her day there were fifteen hundred shops for the sale of intoxicating liquor;* outside Chicago, in Illinois, five hundred. Twenty million dollars were expended annually in the state for intoxicating drink, more than on all schools and universities. In her many years of temperance work she found that "the saloon and the brothel are Siamese twins;" that "the two serpents, intemperance and impurity, must

---

* In New York in 1890 there were seventy-five hundred saloons, one to every two hundred persons.

rise or fall together." Judge Davis of New York, who had been twenty years on the bench, declared that ninety per cent of crime was due to strong drink; insurance statistics of the day showed that the life of the total abstainer was nearly twice that of the moderate drinker.

"The whiskey power," Miss Willard said, "looms like a Chimborazo among the mountains of difficulty over which we must climb to the land of our dreams." Thinking perhaps of her beloved brother Oliver, she said she had seen that power "slowly, imperceptibly wrap men round in its close winding sheet, as if they were Egyptian mummies. They never know their bondage until the first faint movement toward a better life."

To her, high license was a "pitiably inadequate measure, the worst of all schemes for controlling the liquor traffic; those who vote for it lose sight of the fact that they have legalized a traffic that will make necessary the expense of almshouse, hospital, insane aslyum and penitentiary." She called it "moral chloroform."

We believe that, while the poison habits of a nation can be largely restrained by an appeal to the intellect through argument, to the heart through sympathy, and to the conscience through motives of religion, the traffic in those poisons will be best controlled by prohibitory law. We believe the teachings of science, experience and the Golden Rule combine to testify against the traffic in alcoholic liquor, and that the homes of America have no enemy so relentless as the American saloon.

We know that in America the great clanging mill of government turns out just one product, and that is protection for life and property. But the citadel of purity, the palladium of liberty, the home, our brothers have forgotten adequately to protect. Therefore, I speak on behalf of millions of women to ask that the guarantees and safeguards of law shall be stripped from the saloons; that their tarnished gold shall no more pollute our treasury, and that the land we love may at once and forever go out of partnership with the liquor traffic. The liquor traffic is the awful heritage of a less wise, less enlightened past. For its existence in this age we are all more or less responsible. Let us combine to put it away.

When the temperance crusade began, no one would have predicted that twelve years later we should be as earnestly at work for fallen women as for fallen men. That we are, is because we have learned that malt liquors and wines have special power to tarnish the sacred springs of being; that every house of ill-repute is a secret saloon, and nearly every inmate an inebriate. Unnatural and unspeakable crimes against the physically weaker sex make the daily papers read like a modern edition of Fox's *Martyrs*. A madness not exceeded in the worst days of Rome seems to possess the inflamed natures of men let loose from the 250,000 saloons of the nation upon the weak and unarmed women, whose bewildering danger it is to have attracted the savage glances of these men, or to be bound to them by the sacred tie of wife or mother in a bondage worse than that which lashes the living to the dead. In a majority of cases where the gentler sex is thus hunted to its ruin, strong drink is the devil's kindling-wood of passion, as everybody knows.

Appealing to women for union in fighting for temperance, Miss Willard said: "Alone, we can do little; aggregated, we become batteries of power. Agitate, educate, organize—these are the deathless watchwords of success."

Whittier wrote for her marble bust presented by
Lady Henry Somerset to Willard Hall:

> She knew the power of banded ill,
> But felt that love was stronger still,
> And organized for doing good
> The world's united womanhood.

Miss Willard quoted Senator Blair of New Hamp-
shire as saying:

For more than half a century gigantic efforts have been
put forth by noble men and women, by statesmen and by
states, to restrain and destroy the alcohol evil through the
operations of moral suasion and by state law. Public senti-
ment has been aroused and at times it might have been
crystallized had the labor been properly directed. But it
failed, as it always will fail, so long as we save at the spigot
and waste at the bung, if I may borrow a simile from the
business of the enemy. The temperance question is a national question, just as much so as the tariff is and more than
slavery was. It is a waste of time to deal with it only by
towns and counties and states. All possible local efforts
should be put forth against the liquor death everywhere,
(but) what the temperance reform most needs is national-
ization. The nation can act in no other way than by law;
and now there is no national law for the removal of the
alcohol evil. On the contrary, by guaranteeing the importation and transportation and permitting the manufacture, the
national Constitution is the very citadel of the rum power.

In 1915 a marble statue of Miss Willard was placed
in the Hall of Fame in the Capitol Building in Washington. Representative Brooks of Colorado, in paying
tribute to Miss Willard for his State, said; "Today the
nation joins in welcoming the newest addition to our
Hall of Fame. It recognizes and pays glad tribute to

her intellectual ability, her self-sacrificing work for her race, and the grandeur of her moral worth. It takes her into full fellowship with her heroes of war and peace, her great law-makers and administrators, as one of those who have done great things for their native land."

At the time of her admission to the national Hall of Fame, Katharine L. Stevenson wrote:

> How great she stands!
> A mountain-peak her soul;
> An ocean wide; a river sweeping on with full
>   free tide;
> A sacred shrine where holiest things abide;
> How great she stands!

The women of the country can wield immense power for good if they choose so to do; being more numerous than their brothers they can sway the vote in ways to free us from the dominance of the liquor industry, the tavern, the night club and saloon. How tragic when they use their hard-won vote instead to further the forces of evil!

By the simple expedient of abstaining from alcoholic beverages themselves, training their children in the reasons for so doing, and refraining from offering liquor to their guests, women can at the same time restore the purity of the home, renew their influence for good over the male members of the family, and curtail by more than half the power of the distilleries. Women have yet to prove the expediency of the move which yielded them the vote. The challenge of the hour is great; may they be equal to it!

Chapter VII

A PSYCHIATRIST MAKES HIS DEPOSITION

(The following pages 72 to 81 by the eminent Swiss psychiatrist, Professor A. Forel, M. D., Ph. D., LL.D., are from an article which was published in 1900 in *The American Journal of Insanity* and which was heartily endorsed by Dr. Adolf Meyer, Professor Emeritus of Psychiatry, Phipps Clinic, Johns Hopkins University, Baltimore. It is the more authoritative, therefore, in that it represents the conviction of two very distinguished psychiatrists.)

Brought up in the midst of a country of vineyards on the Lake of Geneva, I considered wine an almost indispensable part of human food, being accustomed from childhood to drink some daily. I was given wine to strengthen me, to form blood, and God knows what all. I liked wine moderately taken, because I was accustomed to it, or perhaps because I had an agreeable sensation after it, i.e., was slightly exhilarated. With all that, the wine taverns and the vulgarity of our customs of drinking were an abomination to me, and

I still have a few bad verses of pessimistic satire which I made as a youth and in which I described our people as going to ruin through inebriety.

Thus I grew up. I suffered much from disorders of digestion, especially from cardialgia and headaches, without having an idea that two or three glasses of wine a day might have something to do with it. In 1873 I became assistant of v. Gudden, at the Hospital for the Insane at Munich. There, the drinking of wine was replaced by the drinking of beer, and my disorders of digestion became considerably worse. In 1879, I became director of the Burghölzli Hospital for the Insane and Professor of Psychiatry at Zurich. Fully 25 per cent of the male admissions to my hospital were alcoholics. Later their number rose to 30 per cent. All my efforts to turn them into permanent water drinkers were in vain.

About 1884, I happened to send for a shoemaker to take my measure for shoes. After this was done I offered him a glass of wine as is customary with us. He declined with a smile. I was surprised and asked if he was a total abstainer. "Yes." "You have a society, perhaps." "Yes, I happen to be its chairman." I jumped to my feet. "You are the man for whom I have long been looking. Will you receive into your society the alcoholics who leave the hospital? I should send you the most promising cases." "With pleasure; send me all; one never knows whether the apparently worst ones do not turn out best after all."

From that day every alcoholic who was improving was sent with an attendant to the shoemaker and to the

6

meeting of the society. With a touching self-sacrifice and with the greatest insight the poor man devoted himself to the patients. His recompense was their recovery. As if by a charm, for the first time in my life I saw drunkards recover, truly and lastingly cured. To be sure there were still many relapses, since only the worst ones came to the hospital for the insane, yet his angelic patience could not be discouraged.

One day I said: "Well, dear friend, it is nearly two years now that you have devoted yourself in such a disinterested way to my alcoholics, and that many get well is something I never saw before. Please explain to me how it is. I am paid by the State to cure these people, and I cannot do it. You are the one who cures the drinkers, not I." He answered with a smile: "It is very simple, Director; I am an abstainer and you are not. You cannot teach others convincingly that which you do not do yourself."

From that day I became an abstainer. It is true, I was afraid it might hurt my health, so deep were the roots of prejudice in my head. But the anticipated weakness and anaemia did not come. Instead, I had lost my cardialgia within three months, and within ten years traces of gravel promising gout, and also my formerly frequent headaches. Mental and physical efficiency were increased in a manner not foreseen. I never could have believed that giving up two or three glasses of wine a day could strengthen me to such an extent. From that day, as if freed from an evil charm, I could depend on my own sails and did not need anybody to assist me to cure alcoholics. One must have gone through such a change to fully appreciate the power of example and of the force of one's own consistency in action.

I presided as a convinced abstainer at the Second International Congress against the abuse of alcoholic beverages at Zurich. Even then, the cure of the drinkers appeared to me merely as a first step, as the beginning of a gigantic work of social reform. For what good is it after all, to spend all the time and labor over the mending of ruins, broken down by other ill-advised people? No, the bull must be seized by the horns; the source of evil must be stopped. Abolition of the consumption of alcohol in any form for all humanity was the clear and unequivocal aim of the struggle.

The sophistry and lamentable weakness of the arguments of opponents is so general, so uniform, that this really furnishes in itself the best proof of the truth of the abstainer's standpoint. Were it not for such immense financial interests, such inconceivable prejudices, sanctioned by poetry, songs, and the eminently illusive and alluring effect of alcohol on the brain, one might well despair of the soundness of judgment of the humanity which adheres so tenaciously to the deceptive use of this poison of nations.

Experience shows that in all countries where the alcoholic habit reigns, it accounts for from one half to three fourths of the crimes, a great share of suicides, of mental disorders, of deaths, of diseases generally, of poverty, of vulgar depravity, of sexual excesses and venereal diseases and of dissolution of families. In

Switzerland, careful statistics of the fifteen largest cities show that one third of the male suicides and one tenth of the deaths in men above twenty years are wholly or essentially referable to alcohol. For the male insane I found alcoholism to be the direct cause of one third.

Prof. Demme of Berne, famous as a physician of the diseases of children, not an abstainer, compares the progeny of ten families in which the father, and in a few cases the mother, were drunkards, with that of ten sober families. The ten families of drunkards had fifty-seven children. Of these twelve died very early of weakness, eight became idiots, thirteen epileptics, five dwarfs, five had malformations or were deaf mutes, five became drunkards with chorea or epilepsy—nine only remained normal. The ten sober families had sixty-one children. Of these five died quite small, two suffered from chorea, two were mentally backward but not idiots, fifty remained quite normal. Further we see that of the 2000 idiots and epileptics of the Asylum of Bicêtre near Paris, 75 per cent have one or two alcoholic parents.

I further mention the 709 known descendants of a drinking woman studied by Prof. Peloman in Bonn. Of these 106 were illegitimate, 142 beggars, 64 supported by their townships, 181 prostitutes, 76 convicted criminals (7 of them murderers). This beautiful family cost the State altogether 5,000,000 marks. This is the ultimate consequence of hereditary alcoholic degeneration of the brain.

Well, you say, but alcohol is poisonous in excessive amounts only. A moderate amount of beer or wine will not do any harm; it promotes pleasant sociability, etc. We do not care to forego this pleasure just on account of a few drunkards—the well-known argumentation.

Doses of alcohol which correspond to a glass of wine or a pint of German beer (certainly a most moderate dose) are sufficient to regularly paralyze, retard or disturb all the central and centripetal cerebral functions. The number of mistakes in calculation, setting type, memorizing, etc., is increased. Sensibility is blunted, the reaction is retarded. The subjective consequence is agreeable; one feels heat, cold, pain less; one is less afraid, less accurate, less scrupulous. At the same time a very slight illusional veil spreads over reality, the first beginning of the later intoxication by higher doses. Hence, whenever alcohol promotes sociability and loosens the tongue, it is the consequence of a cerebral intoxication. It may rouse stupid crowds to talk. One only needs to study in Germany the "beer jokes," beer conversation and beer literature. They have stifled in young Germany the idealism, the taste for the classics and the finer mental pleasures throughout broad parts of the nation and in both sexes.

Wherever the drinking habit prevails there are a few really serious people who actually adhere to the moderate limit. The great mass, and with them many people of culture, even scientists, drink more or less immoderately according to the amount of available money or opportunity, are seduced, lose money, strength, time and health, and serve the alcohol dealers as a field of capture. Those more disposed or exposed gradually fall a prey to inebriety, and become abhorrent examples; the others then take the unfortunate victims of their habit as the black sheep of their own sins. Every drinker, one must remember, was moderate once and did not want to become a drunkard. How many die of alcoholism of the heart, or of the liver, or of the kidneys without knowing (the reason for) it! "The moderate drinkers are the unconscious seducers of the people," says Prof. v. Bunge very justly.

When I mentioned this lately to an American scholar, he answered: "Oh, with us in America it is quite different. Only common people drink down their throats; decent people drink only occasionally very moderately with their friends. We rather believe in educating people to a thoughtful and judicious command of their own inclination." To this I answered that this is so; that the drinking habit came into disuse with you is due to those total abstainers and prohibitionists whom you attack so. But if you succeed in destroying their work, you will before long, with your "moderate drinking," introduce again in a short time the European drink-habit in America and the entire campaign may begin anew after you have given progress a setback of from fifty to one hundred years.* He had no answer to this.

Moderate drinking is the nursery of inebriety. It leads to social alcoholism with mathematical certainty

---

* Unhappily Prof. Forel's prognostication was only too accurate. The "decent people" who drank "only occasionally, very moderately with their friends," have in the four decades since then become the immoderate consumers of alcoholic beverages, not only frequently with their friends, but regularly at home before dinner and at other times.

because this is human nature and because we cannot change the human brain. There is no means of removing the alcohol plague except by the abolition of the drinking habit. In brief I know of not one sensible reason which would justify the moderate use of alcoholic beverages (and of other narcotic drugs like cocaine, hashish, opium, morphine, ether, etc.), and, on the other hand, know of innumerable most serious scientific and social reasons which condemn the indulgence very stringently.

I had for a long time felt, and really found substantiated, that the teachers of American universities are either indifferent or are opposed to the Temperance movement. I therefore made an effort to search for the reasons, and was astonished to find with most a great ignorance of the alcohol question and of the social and individual effects of alcohol. There was much adverse criticism of prohibition; that too much religion and too much politics were mixed with the matter, etc. Whenever, however, I asked the critics what they wanted to do positively to improve the situation, most of them were helpless.

The most frequent objection against the prohibition laws is that they are never carried out and lead to corruption. This argumentation is continually rehearsed in the most thoughtless manner. I have always said, "It is illogical to make the prohibition laws responsible for financial corruption and hypocrisy. Nobody will convince me that in license districts and States corruption and hypocrisy are less and laws are better observed."

An earnest friend of reform, but opponent of the prohibition laws, complained to me that the local option drives the scum of inebriety from the no-license to the license towns, which in turn become worse and worse. In this I saw a great advantage. One must take pains to open the eyes of the inhabitants of license towns and lead them to no-license by comparison of their misery with the thriftiness of the no-license towns. The alcohol dealers do not abhor the most corrupt and objectionable means to provoke the violation of the prohibition laws and to fight them, since their pecuniary interests are at stake.

Above all, all legal measures must have a purely restrictive, never a fiscal character, or else they corrupt the State itself. As a final aim, the legislator must always and under all conditions keep in view the total abolition of all distilled and fermented beverages. There is no other sensible or rational aim. The State or the authorities ought never to become interested in the sale of alcohol, in the poisoning of the nation. Alcohol dealers and producers are the enemies of the hygiene and morals of the people, and destroyers of our race. But it is the duty of every good citizen to set a good example, to become an abstainer, and through instruction and practical help, divert all the strata of the population more and more from the drink habit. Yes, it is necessary to become a total abstainer. For as long as one drinks even just one glass a month one feels the irresistible need of excusing and defending that glass, and unconsciously one becomes an advocate of the alcohol habit. To drink alcohol and to fight its social consequences effectually do not go together.

Public opinion must be educated in this sense independent of politics and religion,—the rich and the poor, the educated and the uneducated. In the first place, however, it is the duty of physicians, the guardians of public and individual hygiene. In Europe there are already powerful medical societies of abstainers for this purpose.

One word on the anti-alcoholic instruction in the schools. One should concentrate in it the most important unequivocal statistics and facts which make the use of alcohol so objectionable and dangerous scientifically, socially, hygienically, without mixing them up with other facts of anatomy, of physiology and of hygiene.

Chapter VIII

ECONOMIC ASPECTS OF LIQUOR

Long ago business leaders began to sense the advantages of a sober working force. When George Pullman established his model industrial town in 1880, he banned the drink traffic through his control of the title deeds to the land. The Philadelphia and Reading, the Lake Erie and Western, the Northern Pacific and the Missouri Pacific Railways forbade the use of intoxicants by men on duty. An inquiry by the Federal Commissioner of labor in 1897 showed that 5300 employers out of 7000 habitually enquired into the drinking habits of applicants for jobs, and that 1800 prohibited drinking.*

Today such companies as E. I. du Pont de Nemours & Co., Eastman Kodak Co., Consolidated Edison Co. of New York, Allis Chalmers of Milwaukee, American

---

* *The Rise of the City,* Arthur M. Schlesinger.

Rolling Mill Co. of Middletown, Ohio, are leading the way in trying to do something definite to combat alcoholism among their employees in order to avoid the immense loss, aggregating over a billion dollars to industry as a whole, resulting therefrom.

In an article in Collier's Magazine entitled *My Views on Liquor and the Law* Henry Ford wrote in 1932:

A good deal of criticism has been directed against our company because we insist on sobriety among our men, but I don't know of any company that doesn't. One difference may be that in our company the rule applies from the top down.

It will probably be conceded that I have had some experience with men. I have seen them, high and low, rich and poor, for many years now, and I am no stranger to the effects of drink on all sorts of careers. I have never known a drinker, even a moderate one, if there is such a thing, who has stood the test of crisis. I have seen great corporations in times of prosperity boast of their "liberal" attitude on the liquor question and encourage their responsible men to liberal behavior in that regard: and I have seen those same corporations, when the crisis came, compelled to dismiss those very men who lived by the so-called liberal logic. It simply does not work. My experience with the effects of drink on the family is something that no amount of argument could possibly efface. My feeling toward the man overtaken by this degrading and destructive habit is such that I would go to any lengths to save him. Because I feel that way I cannot as a citizen consent that my government shall be a partner in the business whose best customers are out worst citizens; nor can I consent as a citizen to share the money taken as taxes from a business that makes merchandise of the souls of men.

As to the use of liquor by motorists and those responsible for the management of machinery, it should be unnecessary to say anything. All America knows that liquor and gasoline do not go well together. No one wants any drinking man to be at the mercy of machinery, and no one wants to be at the mercy of any machine in the hands of a drinking man.

Dr. Haven Emerson, in an article written for *The Christian Science Monitor,* states:

Absenteeism from illness related to the use of alcohol is common, particularly on Mondays and the days immediately following holidays. Output is lowered, speed, quantity and quality of product or services are reduced by the inferiority of performance of industrial workers who habitually or intermittently use alcoholic beverages, even if they use them in a way to avoid obvious drunkenness in the police sense of the term.

Society, the wage-earner's family particularly, suffers from the diversion of some seven (now nine) billion dollars annually, for purchase of alcoholic beverages by the consumer, from constructive uses for better housing, feeding of children, clothing, and wholesome recreation.

What the community gets in taxes on the beverage alcohol industry and retail trade does not nearly meet the cost of illness, death, unemployment, accident, crime, and mental disease which are the result of alcohol abuse and for which the community must pay.

Says Dr. E. M. Jellinek of Yale, in *Vital Speeches:*

Of the 3,000,000 alcoholics in the United States, it is estimated that in 1943 1,370,000 were working as skilled and unskilled laborers in industrial pursuits; they lost on an average 22 working days per year, or a total of 30,000,-000 working days; they had 390,000 injuries through accidents and accounted for 4350 fatalities.

The waste resulting from alcoholism, as well as the waste which occurs in dealing with the problem, is great; prevention, education, and the good will of industries and communities are essential for the solution of this problem.

And Andrew C. Ivy, Ph.D., M.D., D.Sc., in *The International Student of Liquor in Life Today:*

There is obviously something wrong with a society that spends only four billion or so to educate and awaken the brain and over nine billion a year to impair the brain and put it to sleep.

In our country today, according to reliable estimates, there are 3,000,000 excessive drinkers whose lives will be shortened, 750,000 chronic alcoholics, 600,000 persons with tuberculosis, and 500,000 with cancer. We spend over nine billion dollars a year on the production of 750,000 alcoholics and thirty million a year to prevent and treat tuberculosis and cancer. We spend over nine billion to produce a disease and only thirty million to prevent and cure two major diseases!

It is strange that alcoholism is the only disease where it is considered illogical and unethical to annihilate the cause. To prevent malaria, we destroy the mosquito; to prevent small-pox, we vaccinate. But to annihilate beverage alcohol is considered an infringement on one's personal liberties.

The real cure of alcoholism does not exist. The disease may be arrested by treatment in those who really desire that it be arrested. But the accumulated evidence reveals the tragic fact that once an alcoholic always an alcoholic. *Complete abstinence* is the only way to prevent a relapse.

There will always be a liquor evil as long as profit is to be derived from making a drinker out of a non-drinker, or by converting a light drinker into a steady drinker. The evil will continue as long as magazines, newspapers, moving pictures and radio continue to present the most appealing advertising ever conceived and with a yearly expenditure of $75,000,000.

If we are going to prevent an increase in the number of excessive drinkers and alcoholics in our country, among whom will be our own children, we must intensively educate and propagandise the fact that alcohol is a narcotic, that drinking is not smart, that a capacity to hold liquor is a dangerous gift, that intoxication is a disgrace and there is nothing funny about it.

Former Mayor La Guardia of New York once stated that 80 per cent of the cases in magistrates' courts were alcoholics, which meant a terrific cost to New York; and City Judge George J. Grellner of St. Louis feels that

Excessive drink is responsible for most of the crime, broken homes, business failures, and juvenile delinquency in St. Louis. 92 per cent of the 10,000 peace-disturbance cases in 1945 were attributable to too much alcohol. Drunkenness is definitely on the increase and it is not confined to persons in the lower income brackets. The rich as well as the poor appear in the City Courts every day as the result of over-indulgence. During the war most persons earned more money than ever before and took to drink with disastrous results. Now that the war is over husbands and wives still hit the bottle with regularity when they begin to get on each other's nerves. The current wave of crime has been induced by alcohol. Before the war, only two alcoholics a year appeared in my court in comparison with one a day now.

Judge J. T. Zottoli, of the Municipal Court of Boston, said in 1940 that over ninety per cent of the adult population of prisons in Massachusetts to which per-

FATHER OF SIX
TS PEN TERM

or Fatal Assault
w At Tavern In

...it isn't the...

...BALTIMORE...

DRINK DID IT, WOMAN SAYS

Ex-WAC Officer Charged With 2 Holdups 'Swears Off'

New York, Jan. 7 (AP)—Mrs. Madelyn Ruth Evans, of Youngstown, Ohio, 29-year-old former WAC officer who police say held up two Broadway area hotels before dawn "because of drink," was held in $5,000 bail tonight, charged with assault and robbery.

'Sex Recrimination And Be Noted In Mrs. Stevens

Bridgeport, Conn., June 29 (AP)—Coroner Theodore E. Steiber held today that Imogene Stevens killed a young submarine sailor in an "aura of sex recrimination, beer and window smashing reprisals" created by a dispute over a neighbor's husband in which the sailor had no part.

The dispute...

two women went to a D ern, announced to the that they intended to until they had consume twenty glasses of beer— and then, joined by Mr went to Imogene's home. The women, whom he said were described by "drunk" when they left he consumed more liquor at ens home. There the "s Mr. Milton's relations Stevens came up for among the three princip the finding, leading to the tion between the two wo

Women's Tempers F
Mrs. Milton, said the "showed her temper" by d ice-pick through one Stevens's windows as she reprisal, he asserted, ed out of her house a glass" through a liv ow of the Milton ho was "more than a prob the coroner, that nd on Mrs. Stevens a oting (police said attached), were inflicted lton.

Mrs. Stevens told police aying that she shot Albe attacked her after she lered him and his brother the house.

"Under Influence Of Li
The coroner said that be ing "under a high emotiona when she killed Albert, ens was also under the infl liquor."

The coroner held, howe "the intoxicated condition Stevens does not absolve of manslaught been held

---

EA CAPTAIN OUND ROBBED DEAD AT CLIFF

hree Being Held In Probe Of Row At Oregon Night Club

Portland, Ore., Jan. 21 (AP)—The eaten body of a 53-year-old sea aptain was found today at the oot of a cliff, over which, police aid, he had been tossed after being robbed.

He was Frank B. Tatum, of Billerica, Mass., and survivor of the S.S. Edwin Abbey and master of the S.S. time torpedoings. He disap m a Portland night club his ship was load

---

Beer Tavern License Denied, Applicant Kills 3 And Himself

Duluth, Minn., Feb. 1 (AP)—An angry storekeeper turned his deer rifle on the five-man town board of the tiny crossroads community of Elmer which had refused him a beer-tavern license yesterday, killed three members, wounded a fourth, then took his own life.

The dead were Frank Svoboda 35, township clerk; Emil Makel 35, board chairman; Albert Dupa 65, a township supervisor. and slayer, Joe A. Contanzi. 32.

Louis Ringhofer, 53

shooting, during which Ringhoft was unded by a bullet fi of an anterio Contanzi ing be

---

Liquor Raid Starts Riot At Horse Show; 1 Dead

Manassas, Va., Sept. 3 (AP)—State Trooper P. P. Herndon said tonight that one man was fatally injured, a policeman cut and ten or twelve persons jailed on charges of inciting to riot today when a crowd attending a horse show spon-sored by Negroes sought to keep himself and two other officers from confiscating a car containing several gallons of whisky.

Arvin Lacy, who was among sev-eral thousand Negroes from several ates attending the horse show. d in Alexandria Hospital tonight a bullet wound in the head. Herndon said was fired by unidentified person. Deputy

---

Chicago Cafe Shooting Investigated By Police

Chicago, Oct. 24 (AP)—Joseph cKnight, 46, former WMC con-tant in Jacksonville, Fla., was in ious condition today as a re-mysterious shooting i tail lounge and has D

Man Dead 2½ Months, Wife 'Just Ignored It'

Boston, May 5 (AP)—The body of a man dead two and a half months was found in a South End tenement today and police quoted his wife as saying "we were both heavy drinkers and I just ignored it."

Police listed him as James Walsh, 53. onard Lilly said the in the apar

---

R BOUT FATAL CLERIC'S WIFE

Dumped Nude Body Into ey, Miami Police Say

ontinued from Page 1)
d to marry as soon as she ed a divorce.

er quoted Smith as saying: st saw her at 8.30 last night. nd a soldier, who had known Boston, and I were having drinks in a bar in the neigh-d.

soldier and I decided that d enough drinks and went up room. We left Ella in the fell asleep. When I woke it bout 1 A.M., and she hadn't home yet.

ooked For Her, He Says
smoked until dawn, and then out looking for her. I called ail to see if she was there, be-I knew she became difficult

---

ALCOHOLISM PRESCRIPTION: QUIT DRINKING

Total Abstinence Is Only Cure, Harvard Psychia-trist Tells Doctors

Richmond, Va., April 14 (AP)—Ever stop to wonder while you bobbed for that olive in the mar-tini just what type of person be-comes the chronic alcoholic?

It can happen to anybody, an authority on the subject said to-night. Anybody, that is, who takes a drink.

Dr. Robert Fleming, of Harvard Medical School's psychiatry de-partment, discussed it here before a five-state seminar on mental and nervous disorders.

Why People Go In For Drinking the way Dr. Fleming

Abducted By Drunk Gunm 3 Expectant GI Mothers

Columbus, Ga., May 5 (AP)—A drunken man in an automobile ab-ducted three expectant mothers—one expecting her b in a week—and held them up for twelve hours, the frighten women reported today.

The three returned home by and related their experiences army investigators at near-by For Benning, where their husbands are stationed. They had been missing since 11 A.M. yesterday.

They said their abductor, drink-ing heavily, brandished an auto-mate pistol and threatened to use it "if necessary."

He was so drunk they added, that keep running off the road and uttering to himself, "Dammit, straighten up."

When He Stopped For Gas
er twelve hours of terror, they hey managed to escape about ock last night. The man, they stopped at a filling sta- ear the Georgia-Florida to get gasoline. ted a fight with the sta- er over the price of the While he was thus en- ran first into a rest- they slipped out and he road.

Alcoholi Ho

Memb cll's alcohol last Lob

GI In Stuttgart Runs Amok, Kil

Stuttgart, Germany, May 1—An American soldier ran today and killed three persons Army said.

Military police headquarters Recruit Russell Jones, of River, Mass., a military police went to a motor pool, in an i icated condition, to get a jee displaced person acting as a g refused him permission. The dier, MP's said, seized the gu carbine and shot him.

Then, the military police acc continued, Jones drove off in jeep and stopped two Germah g When they refused, the Army s he killed one of them. The ot entered the jeep later but escap by a ruse.

In Schweldingen, the MP's w on. Jones wrecked the jeep in

Alcohol-induced Crime

sons are sent for misdemeanors are there for offenses caused by drunkenness, and about fifty per cent of persons sentenced to penal institutions committed offenses related to alcoholism.

Referring to a measure taken in the past to reduce the number of such offenders and at the same time reduce the enormous governmental expense of trying them and carrying them in penal institutions and hospitals, Samuel McCune Lindsay, Prof. Emeritus of Social Legislation at Columbia University, in an article in the *Encyclopaedia Britannica,* 1929, said:

National prohibition was adopted as the logical result of a long experience with State and local prohibition. . . . The amendment cannot truthfully be said to have been "put over" by any fanatical minority. It was adopted after full and free public discussion, in the face of determined and powerful opposition, by larger majorities and greater unanimity in Congress and in the 46 States which ratified it than any other amendment. . . . Dr. Ernest H. Cherrington in the *Annals,* Amer. Acad. of Pol. and Social Science, Sept. 1923, says: "No amendment ever received as strong official sanction by the States as the 18th amendment. The original Constitution was adopted in the 13 original States by a majority of about two to one. The aggregate vote in the State senates and State houses of representatives for the ratification of the 18th amendment shows a majority of more than four to one."

State-wide prohibition was the law in 33 States at the time the amendment went into effect. 90% of the townships and rural precincts, 85% of the counties and over 75% of the villages of the United States were under prohibition by state legislation. Local option and State prohibition had put 68.3% of the population and 95.4% of the land area under prohibition and the amendment and subsequent legislation really affected radically only 31.7% of the population and 4.6% of the area of the United States.

New scientific knowledge had emphasized the menace to health and efficiency and the frightful cost and waste inherent in the consumption of alcoholic beverages in even moderate quantities. New industrial economics did not seem to find any place for alcoholic beverages in working out the problems of the expansion and large-scale production of American industry, trade and commerce. . . . Long before the United States entered the World War the conviction was growing that social and industrial efficiency, and even national prosperity, could not be achieved at any less cost than whatever sacrifices might be involved in national prohibition.

There has been no little controversy over the cost of enforcing national prohibition. As a matter of dollars and cents, it is probable that the Federal tax-payer could well afford greatly to increase, if necessary, the expenditure for the enforcement of prohibition without incurring any tax burden, in view of increased economic benefits accruing therefrom.

The low-priced automobile, home ownership, an expansion of the family budget so that it includes much that formerly was the luxury of the few, the increase in investment of surplus earnings in income-producing shares in the working capital of the country, are all factors in the welfare of thousands of families to which prohibition has made a contribution.

In 1925, Herbert Hoover, then Secretary of Commerce, said; "There can be no doubt of the economic benefits of prohibition. Viewing the temperance question only from this angle, prohibition has proved its case. I think increased temperance over the land is responsible for a good share of the enormously increased efficiency in production, which statistics gathered by the Department of Commerce show to have followed passage of the dry law. Exhaustive study from many angles of production, indicates that while our productivity should have increased about fifteen per cent due to the increase in population, the actual increase has been from twenty-five to thirty per cent."

In "Is Prohibition a Blow at Personal Liberty?" published in *The Ladies' Home Journal,* May 1919, William Howard Taft enumerates among the several classes to whom the overwhelming adoption of the 18th Amendment was due:

1st, The employers, the success of whose enterprises was dependent on the degree of efficiency of the workmen employed. The stringency of the rules against inebriety in great establishments increased much in the late decades;

2nd, Men of all walks of society who resented the political strength and truculence and the demoralizing and corrupting influence in legislatures and even in Congress of the saloon keepers and liquor dealers' associations.

There are many who might drink liquor and be moderate in its use. But we must recognize that liquor is a very considerable source in stimulating crime,—that it plays a large part in the production of poverty and suffering not only for the excessive drinker himself but for those dependent on him. Such a man in many ways imposes a burden on society at large. The restraint of the liberty of the individual to whom the use of intoxicants is enjoyable is but a slight restriction on his general freedom of action. It is something he may very well be called upon to give up to save for society those whom it depraves and destroys.

The drinking of liquor is a social practice and is increased in a very large degree by the opportunity of access for many who would never drink at all unless it was set under their noses by the infesting presence of saloons in their com-

7

munity. The political machine of saloon-keepers and liquor dealers wields, through the ubiquitous saloon, a pernicious influence upon voters.

This array of the immoral and vicious effects of the free manufacture and sale of liquor upon the community can leave no doubt that the curtailment of personal freedom in effective prohibition is small as compared with its benefit to society.

The Amendment has been adopted, and with all good citizens I am in favor of the enactment of the most practical laws to secure the rigid enforcement. A citizen who is in favor of the enforcement of only the laws for which he has voted is not a law-abiding citizen of a democracy. He is not willing to play the game according to the rules of the game. Therefore, whatever my previous view, I am strongly in favor now of putting the Amendment to a test as favorable as possible for its successful operation.

Some of the domestic evils of drunkenness are houses without windows, gardens without fences, fields without tilling, barns without roofs, children without clothing, principles, morals or manners.

—Benjamin Franklin

If a natural choice between drunkenness and sobriety were possible in our civilization, I should leave the people free to choose. But when I see an enormous capitalist organization pushing drink under people's noses at every corner, and pocketing the price, whilst leaving me and others to pay the colossal damages, then I am prepared to smash that organization and make it as easy for a poor man to be sober, if he wants to, as it is for his dog.

—George Bernard Shaw in
The Civic Bulletin, November 1947.

In 1947 Americans spent on alcoholic
beverages (estimate of the Dept. of Commerce) $9,640,000,000

Cost to themselves and to society annually
of the 3,750,000 chronic and excessive
drinkers thus produced (estimate in *Amer.
Journal of Public Health*) $1,000,000,000

Annual cost to industry of alcoholic employees (estimate of Dr. Anton Carlson
of University of Chicago............. $1,000,000,000

Cost of the at least one-fifth of the traffic
accidents, 1946, due to drink (estimate of
the National Safety Council).......... $440,000,000
_____
$12,080,000,000

In 1946-47 Americans spent for all public
and private schools, colleges, universities,
professional and normal schools, schools
for delinquents, blind, deaf, mentally de-
ficient, Indians, and school libraries (estimate of the Office of Education)....... $4,586,000,000

For public libraries, 1944-45.......... $61,790,307

For gifts to religious bodies, 1946...... $1,249,900,000

For American Red Cross, 1947........ $119,055,205
_____
$6,016,745,512

While we are spending on liquor more than twice what we
spend on education, the National Education Ass'n reports
a school crisis,—hundreds of sub-standard teachers, insuf-
ficient enrollment of teacher training institutions, over-
crowded school buildings, millions of children failing to get
the kind of education they need.

In 1947, reported arrests for drunkenness.... 1,216,507

For drunken driving....................   71,886

For disorderly conduct (all highest of record).   307,867

Liquor law violations...................   26,180

Total of reported arrests for violations of law
connected with liquor (not counting those for   ————————
innumerable liquor-induced crimes)......... 1,622,440

Of these offences directly attributable to alcohol, the ratio per 100,000 of the population
was

  In 1932   1,726
  In 1947   3,195

As drinking increases, the number of major
crimes (which include rape, murder, burglary,
etc.) also increases. Estimated total of such
crimes occurring

  In 1943 1,381,681
  In 1948 1,686,676

In Central Union Mission in Washington practically
every civilian who applies for relief has drink as his basic
problem, and in its Children's Emergency Home fifty children out of fifty-four had a record of drinking in the family.

CHAPTER IX

THE BUGLE CALL

Inflaming wine, pernicious to mankind,
Unnerves the limbs, and dulls the noble mind.
—Homer's *Iliad,* 9th cen. B.C.,
trans. by Pope.

The most astonishing anachronism of an age beyond
all others remarkable for its advance and application
of science is its utter failure to apply science and common sense to the extermination of the most ancient and
persistent enemy of the human race: an enemy who
from time immemorial has diverted the course of history, uncrowned kings, lost the battles, corrupted the
politics, inspired a large proportion of the delinquency,
disorder and crime that burden the courts; and caused
a great share of the accidents, disease, and mental
affections that overflow the hospitals of the world: an
enemy who has cut short careers of fairest promise,
wrecked the homes, brutalized the fathers and un-
mothered the mothers of men. An enemy all the more
formidable in that his onslaughts are insidious, his advances attended with passing pleasure and embraced in
a speedy capitulation.

As soon as scientists had denounced the swamp, the mosquito and the housefly as the breeding-place and carrier of disease, we set ourselves to rid our premises of the nuisances. The causes of typhoid and of other epidemics were tirelessly hunted down; those of cancer and the common cold are anxiously and at great expense still being sought. But the entirely obvious agent of the evil that makes the costliest inroads upon our physical, mental, moral and economic welfare goes unchecked and uncondemned by the great masses of mankind.

The English Minister of Health, the United States Public Health Service, the Food and Drug Administration restrict and forbid the use and circulation of other harmful drugs and dangerous foods; but the depressant, poisonous narcotic drug which is present to a greater or less degree in all alcoholic beverages is silently sanctioned by the authorities and allowed to eat deeply into the structure of all that is best in our civilization.

There is much agitation nowadays about the alcoholic's being a "diseased" rather than a degenerate person; but the discussion is entirely beside the point. The simple fact remains, if there were no alcohol available, there would be no alcoholism. If three to four million United States citizens had become "diseased" through the absorption of arsenic, the obvious conclusion would be that arsenic on the general market should no longer be allowed. Dr. G. H. Gehrmann, medical director of du Pont Company, in a discussion

with a fellow doctor who insisted that "alcoholism is
a symptom and we've got to get at what causes it," put
the matter in a nutshell when he replied, "Drinking
out of a bottle causes it." It would be well if, though
late, we would apply to the case some of the wisdom
of the untutored Cayuga Indians who, when in Council
with an official British mission in 1748, were "politely
offered" a cask of rum. They returned it with the message: "We have drunk too much of your rum already,
which has occasioned our destruction; we will, in the
future, beware of it." Another Indian too, of a different sort, has shown us the way: "If I were appointed
dictator for one hour for all India," said Gandhi once,
"the first thing I would do would be to close without
compensation all liquor shops, destroy all toddy palms."

The doctor, the minister, the teacher, the social
worker; the policeman, magistrate and judge, have
ostensibly been trying to allay disease, promote morality, impart knowledge, relieve distress, maintain
order, adjudicate criminal cases; but they have made
no concerted effort to annihilate the prolific cause of
the evils they profess to deplore, the common enemy
of the good they propose to bring about; and so they
fight a losing battle, with evil ever in the lead. Too
often those who might be most influential in the warfare,—the doctor and the minister, connive with the
enemy in that they shrink from publicly denouncing
a drug in which they privately indulge. Surely there
is little ground for attributing either intelligence or
consecration to the doctor, psychiatrist and minister
who, though "alcoholism and heavy social drinking are
increasing" (to use the words of one of them), treat

the alcoholic, but make no effort to eliminate alcohol from our economy.

There is a test for insanity in which the patient is given mop and bucket and told to sop up the water running to the floor from an open faucet. According as he first turns the water off or first begins to mop, he is pronounced sensible or insane. Shall we continue to use a futile mop, or shall we not first turn the faucet off?

Alcohol is a cause, direct or indirect, of gastritis, multiple neuritis, cirrhosis of the liver, tuberculosis, epilepsy; degeneracy, mental disorders and maladjustments and insanity; under its influence an estimated ninety per cent of venereal infections occur; it reduces resistance to most other ills, and through poisoning, chronic or acute, is a major cause of death.

To it can be traced a large proportion of the divorces and of the poverty, malnutrition and crowded housing that prevail; it induces absenteeism, idleness, incompetence and debauchery; it fills the columns and clutters the advertising pages of the daily press and causes from forty to sixty per cent of the fatal highway accidents that occur. It jams the police courts with the disorderly and criminal cases that consume so much of our time and attention and add so heavily to the taxpayer's burden.

If these are some of the positive fruits of the vine, there are too its negative, but equally momentous effects, the loss of money and time to a destructive habit;—money that might be spent for the enrichment of life through wholesome recreation, music, art and literature; time which could be utilized for the collecting of those spiritual goods which, if only our eyes be not dimmed by our servitude to the senses, we see and know to be the only real goods; time for the contemplation of the beautiful, the true, the excellent which Schiller tells us is the immediate possession of those qualities; time for the shedding of that beauty, excellence and enjoyment round about, the neglect of which is our own as well as others' bitter loss. The prophets of old, with John the Baptist, who came drinking neither wine nor strong drink, and all mystics of later date down to Mahatma Gandhi have known that those who seek the higher levels of life naturally abjure the drugs that deaden thought, dull the enthusiasm (entheos, *the God in us*), and blur the beatific vision.

It is surely a solemnizing thought that the friend to whom we offer a drink may be a candidate for alcoholism; that the best of us, after a friendly 'old-fashioned' or two, stepping into our cars, are potential murderers on the highway; that after the third and fourth drink, which follow too easily upon the first and second, we may, like Alexander, turn upon our dearest friend or next of kin, and only when he lies dying at our feet, be stricken with undying remorse at what we have done. That this is not a fantastic impossibility we may see by running through the next few accounts of murder that we come upon in the morning paper till we reach the oft-repeated words, *had been drinking, had visited several taverns, had had three beers.* These were not premeditated murders for the most part, but committed in the heat of drink by persons not very unlike ourselves, mistaken only in thinking that they could remain moderate in drink.

Considering the initial ideals of the founders of America and the phenomenal opportunities open to us in the freedom of our much-boasted democracy, is it not tragic that two visitors from overseas could pass upon us the following indictment?

J. B. Priestley, British novelist and playwright, found in New York "a deep sense of unease, disquiet, of the restless, homeless heart. It is filled with people who, after three quick drinks, begin to dream of somewhere else." Cyril Connolly, gifted editor of London's literary and artistic magazine *Horizon,* came to America to understand and love the Americans. But he found even rich Americans were "gloomy." Alcohol floods and clogs them to such an extent that there is "a drunk in every respectable family." So after midnight many Americans "fight or weep." The most striking feature of American society appeared to be the "immense rush to psychiatry, the high rate of madness and suicide."

Europeans consider Americans the greatest drinkers in the world, who consume hard liquor, says Geneviève Tabouis, to liberate themselves from the puritanical taboos that still remain; to escape, says de Rougemont, to "cheap artificial paradises." Americans find a drunken man laughable; Europeans think him disgraceful, particularly if of the upper class.

Other keen Europeans find our leading trait to be our susceptibility to the propaganda designed for our endless exploitation by avaricious industries, aided by all the cunning of professional psychologists. We fall, unthinking and easy victims, to the vast, nationwide advertising campaigns launched by liquor and cigarette manufacturers whose sole aim is to fill their coffers at the expense of the utter demoralization of the customer, described by Labarthe as a kind of robot whose mental age is about fourteen.*

The day after the election in 1932, the *Brewery News* said: "Not one-tenth of 1 per cent of the youth of America know the taste of real beer—we must educate them." And the *Brewer's Digest,* May 1941, stated: "One of the finest things that could have happened to the Brewery Industry was the insistence by high ranking officers to make beer available at Army camps. Here is the chance for brewers to cultivate a taste for beer in millions of young men who will eventually constitute the largest beer-consuming section of our population."

With large numbers of our young men abroad, the liquor industry next set out to net youths of college age by offering scholarships to college. Elderly people were advised by them that liquor was helpful in sustaining the aging heart.† Children are being conditioned for later drinking by full-page colored advertisements of liquor usually embodying arresting pic-

---

* *As Others See Us,* by Andre Visson.

† Comp. Dr. Cabot's statement, p. 39: "Alcohol never supported any heart, elderly or young, and never will."

tures of dogs, a leaping horse, bears, or other animals: and a new "beer" has been devised for them resembling exactly in its bottles and labels adult beer, but with alcoholic content low enough to permit it to be sold without license to anyone; the object being to cash in on the child's passion for playing "grown-up" and head it toward stronger drink when it comes of age.

A large bill-board recently seen depicts a bridegroom about to perform the traditional act of bearing the bride, still in her bridal array, across the threshold of the new home. But he pauses; "First things first!" The case of beer there shown must be carried in before the bride!

The so-called "upper class" is setting the drinking pattern in the United States; the women control the fashions in that class; they can, like the wife of President Hayes, openly abandon a custom "more honored in the breach than the observance," which with horrible momentum is shattering the health and mental and moral fibre of the nation. Each hostess doing so, makes it easier for the next and saves her guests from the predicament they so dread of saying No. Each guest daring to decline the proffered drink makes it easier for the rest to do so. What wonders the doctors and ministers could achieve if they would tell all they know of the ravages of the drug, and, above all, if they would themselves abstain from its use! What could we not all do, each in his separate star, if we took the cause to heart and valued our own and others' welfare beyond our passing pleasure!

Even the least strait-laced Episcopal clergyman prefers that the engineer of the train or the pilot of the plane that takes him to his destination should totally abstain from befuddling drink. Has he considered that his parishoner, even while offering him a glass of sherry, would have more confidence in him, the pilot of his soul, if he would decline the drink? The minister's task is as delicate as the aviator's and demands for its best performance faculties more sensitive and creative still. He can not afford to be even by one glass of sherry less spiritually fit.

The "moderate" drinkers particularly could by abstaining be of use because, while addicts in the United States number in the millions, they are numbered by the tens of millions and are the mainstay of the corrupt liquor industry. If really moderate they are still able to abstain, whereas their unfortunate brothers and sisters the addicts cannot regain their liberty without much understanding and enlightened help.

We can all, by abstaining voluntarily, set the example so easy to set. We can cease to pervert the kindly fruits and foliage of the earth into agents of evil for the temptation of our fellow-man, and release them instead for the sustenance of those who are in need.

We can make it unfashionable, shoddy, shameful, quite the reverse of "smart" to offer to others what may be their undoing; and outlaw as uncivilized, unscientific and unchristian the manufacture, circulation and consumption of alcoholic drink.

"Liquor," said Lincoln, "has many defenders, but no defence." There is no possible argument for its continuance, there is every possible reason for its discard. What has been since the dawn of history need not therefore always be; otherwise all progress would be ruled out. Scientists of the day constantly assert that man now holds his evolution for better or for worse in his own hands and can give it the direction he desires. It has become a matter of conscience now whether we shall advance in the scale or recede toward our animal ancestry. Other tyrants are going or gone; this worst tyrant of all, whose despotism cuts most deeply into our private liberty, whose slaves are the most pitiful and abject of any, must go too.

We summon you then, in God's name, all ministers, physicians, teachers, welfare workers, particularly all leaders of fashion and followers of it, to join with all who have the physical, mental and moral good of men at heart and take your place in the Crusade for Science versus insanity, Health versus disease and disaster, Purity versus pollution, Liberty versus servitude. We can, and with God's help we shall, win our emancipation!

This is a Crusade quite as glorious as any of mediaeval times; this would be a revolution the most peaceful and fruitful of any or all times. We can, if we only will, without arms or bloodshed, crowd this thing out which from time immemorial has been the curse and scourge of mankind. The call is imperative, the cause a great one, the moment to begin is NOW.

PART II

A CLOUD OF WITNESSES

The vine bears three kinds of grapes: the first of pleasure, the second of intoxication, the third of disgust.
—Anacharsis (c. 638-559 B.C.)

PLATO

(427?–347 B.C.)

Athenian: Does the drinking of wine heighten and increase pleasures and pains, passions and loves?

Cleinias: Very greatly.

Ath.: And are perception and memory, and opinion and prudence, heightened and increased? Do not these qualities entirely desert a man if he becomes saturated with drink?

Cle.: Yes, they entirely desert him.

Ath.: Does he not return to the state of soul in which he was when a young child?

Cle.: He does.

Ath.: Then at that time he will have the least control over himself?

Cle.: The least.

Ath.: And will he not be in a most wretched plight?

Cle.: Most wretched.

Ath.: Then not only an old man but also a drunkard becomes a second time a child? Is there any argument which will prove to us that we ought to encourage a taste for drinking instead of doing all we can to avoid it?

—Laws I, 645 D.

XENOPHON

(*c.* 400 B.C.)

Socrates speaking:

If, my friends, when a war was coming upon us, we should wish to choose a man by whose exertions we might ourselves be preserved, and might gain mastery over our enemies, should we select one whom we knew to be unable to resist gluttony, or wine, or sensuality? Or if, at the close of life, we should wish to commit to any one the guardianship of our sons, or the care of our unmarried daughters, or the preservation of our property, should we think an intemperate man worthy of confidence for such purposes? Should we trust to an intemperate slave our herds, our granaries, or the superintendence of our agriculture?

But if we would not accept an intemperate slave, how can it be otherwise than important for every man to take care that he does not himself become such a character? The intemperate man, while mischievous to others, is still more mischievous to himself, if it is indeed mischievous in the highest degree to ruin not only his family, but his body and mind. In society too, who could find pleasure in the company of such a man, who felt more delight in eating and drinking than in intercourse with his friends, and preferred the company of harlots to that of his fellows?

Is it not the duty of every man to consider that temperance is the foundation of every virtue, and to establish the observance of it in his mind before all things? Who that is a slave to pleasure is not in an ill condition both as to body and mind? It appears to me, by Juno, that a freeman ought to pray that he may never meet with such a character, and that he who is a slave to pleasure should pray to the gods that he may find well-disposed masters; for by such means only can a man of that sort be saved.

—*Memorabilia of Socrates,* I, v, 1-5.

Socrates questions Euthydemus:
Tell me, Euthydemus, do you regard liberty as an excellent and honorable possession for an individual or a community?

8

The most excellent and honorable that can be.

Do you consider him who is held under control by the pleasures of the body, and is rendered unable, by their influence, to do what is best for him, to be free?

By no means.

Do not the intemperate, then, appear to you to be absolutely without freedom?

Yes, by Jupiter!

And do the intemperate appear to you to be merely prevented from doing what is best, or to be forced also to do what is most dishonorable?

They appear to me to be no less forced to do the one than they are hindered from doing the other.

And what sort of masters do you consider those to be who hinder men from doing what is best, and force them to do what is worst?

The very worst possible.

And what sort of slavery do you consider to be the worst?

That under the worst masters.

Do not the intemperate, then, endure the very worst slavery?

ibid, IV, v, 2-6.

A sensual and intemperate youth hands over a worn-out body to old age.

—Cicero (106-43 B.C.)

There is no small pleasure in pure water.

—Ovid (43 B.C.-A.D. 17)

Drunkenness is nothing but voluntary madness.

—Seneca (4 B.C.-A.D. 65)

GALEN

(c. A.D. 130–c. 200)

(*After Hippocrates he was the most distinguished physician of antiquity*):

Does not wine act like a tyrant, forbidding the mind to think as carefully and to act as correctly as it formerly did, and was it not for this reason that Plato tells us to avoid it as an enemy? For if it once gets into the body, it prevents the steersman from handling the ship's rudder properly, and the soldiers from keeping order in the ranks; it makes judges vacillate when they ought to be just; it makes presidents rule badly and impose unsound ordinances. Plato considers, in fact, that wine fills the whole body, and especially the head, with hot fumes, thus causing immoderate motion in the appetitive and irascible parts of the mind, and hasty judgment in the rational part.

For drunkenness is very sepulture
Of manne's wit and his discretion.
—Chaucer (1340-1400), *The Pardoner's Tale.*

Take especial care that thou delight not in wine; for there never was any man that came to honour or preferment that loved it; for it transformeth a man into a beast, decayeth health, poisoneth the breath, destroyeth natural heat, deformeth the face and maketh a man contemptible.

—Sir Walter Raleigh (1552-1618),
Instruction to His Son.

Long quaffing maketh a short life.
—John Lyly (1554-1606), *Euphues.*

Shall I, to please another wine-sprung mind,
Lose all mine own?
—George Herbert (1593-1633).

Wine hath drowned more men than the sea.
—Thomas Fuller (1608-1661), *Gnomologia.*

SAMUEL BUTLER

(1612–1680)

'Tis pity *Wine,* which Nature meant
To Man in kindness to present,
Should (like the Cyder-tree in Eden,
Which only grew to be forbidden)
No sooner come to be enjoy'd
But th'Owner's fatally destroy'd;
And Man himself with Wine possest
More savage than the wildest Beast,
Supplies his loss of Wit and Sense
With Barbarousness and Insolence;

Believes himself, the less he's able,
The more heroic and formidable;
Lays by his Reason in his Bowls,
As Turks are said to do their Souls,
Until it has so often been
Shut out of its Lodging and let in,
At length it never can attain
To find the right Way back again;
And that which Nature did intend
T' enlarge his Life, perverts t' its End.
So Noah, when he had anchor'd safe on
The mountain's Top, his lofty Haven,
And all the Passengers he bore
Were on the New World set ashore,
He made it then his chief Design
To plant and propagate a Vine
Which since has overwhelm'd and drown'd
Far greater Numbers, on dry Ground,
Of wretched Mankind, one by one,
Than all the Flood before had done.
                    —*Satire on Drunkenness*

LA FONTAINE

(1621–1695)

L'IVROGNE ET SA FEMME

Chacun a son défaut, où toujours il revient:
        Honte ni peur n'y remédie.
    Sur ce propos, d'un conte il me souvient:
        Je ne dis rien que je n'appuie
    De quelque exemple. Un suppôt de Bacchus
Altérait sa santé, son esprit, et sa bourse.

Telles gens n'ont pas fait la moitié de leur course
        Qu'ils sont au bout de leurs écus.
Un jour que celui-ci, plein du jus de la treille,
Avait laissé ses sens au fond d'une bouteille,
Sa femme l'enferma dans un certain tombeau.
        Là les vapeurs du vin nouveau
Cuvèrent à loisir. A son réveil il treuve *
L'attirail de la mort à l'entour de son corps,
        Un luminaire, un drap des morts.
"Oh!" dit-il, "qu'est ceci? Ma femme est-elle veuve?"
Là-dessus, son épouse, en habit d'Alecton,†
Masquée, et de sa voix contrefaisant le ton,
Vient au prétendu mort, approche de sa bière,
Lui présente un chaudreau ‡propre pour Lucifer.
L'époux alors ne doute en aucune manière
        Qu'il ne soit citoyen d'enfer.
"Quelle personne es-tu?" dit-il à ce fantôme.
        "La cellerière § du royaume
De Satan," reprit-elle; "et je porte à manger
        A ceux qu'enclôt la tombe noire."
        Le mari repart sans songer:
        "Tu ne leur portes point à boire?"

SAMUEL PEPYS

(1633–1703)

Pepys the epicure naïvely congratulates himself on
what a condition it hath pleased God to bring me that

---

* Old form of *trouver*.
† One of the three Furies.
‡ =*potage chaud*.
§ =Provisioner.

From the drawing by Gavarni   Courtesy of Walters Art Gallery, Baltimore

I have two tierces of Claret, two quarter casks of Canary, and a smaller vessel of Sack; a vessel of Tent, another of Malaga, and another of white wine, all in my wine cellar together; which I believe none of my friends ever had of his owne at one time;

nevertheless, with his matchless candor, he confides to his faithful Diary *this record of his making and breaking of vows to free himself from the lure of the vine:*

Mar. 10, 1660: All night troubled in my thoughts how to order my business upon this great change with me that I could not sleep, and being overheated with drink I made a promise the next morning to drink no strong drink this week, for I find it makes me sweat and puts me quite out of order.

Aug. 8:—Thence I, having my head full of drink from having drunk so much Rhenish wine in the morning, and more in the afternoon, came home and so to bed, not well, and very ill all night.

Aug. 10: I had a great deal of pain all night so I could not sleep.

Aug. 11: I rose today without any pain, which makes me think that my pain yesterday was nothing but from my drinking too much the day before.

April 2, 1661: (*after drinking with Sir W. Batten, Pen and others*):—Strange how these men, who at other times are all wise men, do now, in their drink, bewitt and reproach one another with their former conditions and their actions as in public concernments, till I was ashamed to see it.

May 14:—Finding my head grow weak nowadays if I come to drink wine, and therefore hope that I shall leave it off of myself, which I pray God I could do.

June 5:—There we staid talking and singing and drinking great drafts of claret till near midnight; and so to bed, very near fuddled.

June 6: My head hath aked all night, and all this morning, with my last night's debauch.

July 26: Having the beginning of this week made a vow to myself to drink no wine this week (finding it to unfit me to look after business) and this day breaking of it against my will, I am much troubled for it, but I hope God will forgive me.

Sept. 29: At dinner and at supper I drink I know not how, of my own accord, so much wine that I was even almost foxed, and my head aked all night; so home and to bed without prayers, which I never did yet, of a Sunday night: I being now so out of order that I durst not read prayers for fear of being perceived by my servants in what case I was.

Jan. 26, 1662: Thanks be to God, since my leaving drinking of wine, I do find myself much better, and do mind my business better, and do spend less money, and less time lost in idle company.

April 7: Went to Mr. Rawlinson's house and there had a good dinner of cold meat and good wine, but I was troubled in my head after the little wine I drank, and so home to my office, and there did promise to drink no more wine but one glass a meal till Whitsuntide next upon any score.

April 25: Was much troubled in my eyes, by reason of the healths I have this day been forced to drink.

June 28: My mind is now in a wonderful condition of quiet and content, more than ever in my life, since my minding the business of my office, which I have done most constantly; and I find it to be the very effect of my late oaths against wine and plays, which, if God please, I will keep constant in, for now my business delights me, and brings me great credit.

July 31: I drank but two glasses of wine this day, and yet it makes my head ake all night, and indisposed me all the next day.

Aug. 7:—It being become a pleasure to me now-a-days to follow my business, and the greatest part may be imputed to my drinking no wine, and going to no plays.

Aug. 17: I walked an hour in the Temple garden, reading my vows, which it is a great content to me to see how I am a changed man in all respects for the better, since I took them, which the God of Heaven continue to me, and make me thankful for.

Aug. 20: I do find my nature ready to run back to my old course of drinking and staying from my business, and yet, thank God, I was not fully contented with it, but did stay at little ease.

Sept. 17: I could not avoid drinking of five glasses this afternoon.

Sept. 29: (Michelmas day) This day my oaths for drinking of wine and going to plays are out, and so I resolve to take a liberty today, and then to fall to them again.

Sept. 30: Good God! how I do find myself by yesterday's liberty hard to be brought to follow business again, but however, I must do it, considering the great sweet pleasure and content of mind that I have had since I did leave drink and plays.

Oct. 31: I thank God I have no crosses, but only much business to trouble my mind with. In all other things as happy a man as any in the world. . . . And all I do impute almost wholly to my late temperance since my making of my vowes against wine and plays.

Dec. 30:—After dinner drinking five or six glasses of wine, which liberty I now take till I begin my oath again.

Jan. 5, 1663: I took Sir W. Batten and Captain Allen into the wine cellar and there drank a great variety of wines, more than I have drunk at one time, or shall again a great while, when I come to return to my oaths, which I intend in a day or so.

Jan. 6: I do find my mind so apt to run to its old want of pleasures, that it is high time to betake myself to my late vows, which I will tomorrow, God willing, perfect and bind myself to.

Sept. 11: I ate well but drank no wine which keeps me in such good order that I am mightily pleased with myself for it.

Sept. 14: My wife, by drinking some cold beer, being hot herself, presently begins to be sick, and became so pale, and I alone with her, that I thought she would have died; and so in great horror, and having a tryall of my true love and passion for her, called the mistresse of the house, and so with some strong water, . . . after a little . . . she came to be pretty well again.

Oct. 20: No extraordinary discourse of anything, every man being intent upon his dinner, and myself willing to have drunk some wine . . ., but I did for my oath's sake willingly refrain it, but am so well pleased and satisfied afterwards thereby, for it do keep me always in so good a frame of mind that I hope I shall not ever leave this practice.

Dec. 31: Tomorrow my vowes are all out as to plays and wine, but I hope I shall not be long before I come to new ones, so much good, and God's blessing, I find to have attended them.

Sept. 15, 1665:—thence with Captain Cocke, and drank a cup of good drink, which I am fain to allow myself during this plague time, by advice of all, and contrary to my oathe, my physician being dead and chyrurgeon out of the way, whose advice I am obliged to take. (*Note that Pepys is as clever as most drinkers in inventing illogical reasons for continually breaking his "oathe"; and, in the following entries, he takes as cruel a delight in seeing others drunk, and is as thoroughly inconsistent in desiring in his servant a sobriety not his own.*)

Sept. 16: Walked to the office; but find myself through . . . my coming from great dinners, and drinking wine, that I am not in the good temper of doing business now a days that I used to be and still ought to be.

Nov. 15:—to Glanville's, where I knew Sir John Robinson, Sir G. Smith and Captain Cocke were gone; and there I made them, against their resolutions, to stay till it was almost midnight, and a furious, darke and rainy, and windy, stormy night; and which was best, I, with drinking small beer, made them all drunk drinking wine, at which Sir John Robinson made great sport.

Dec. 21:—away home, my head full of business and some trouble for letting my accounts go so far that I have made an oathe this night for the drinking no wine, etc. till I have passed my accounts and cleared all.

June 6, 1666: All the afternoon at home doing some business, drawing up my vowes for the rest of the yeare to Christmas; but Lord! to see in what a condition of happiness I am, if I would but keepe myself so; but my love of pleasure is such, that my very soul is angry with itself for my vanity in so doing.

June 12:—Thence to Hale's by coach, it being the seventh day from my making my late oathes and by them I am at liberty to dispense with any of my oathes every seventh day after I had for six days before going performed all my vowes.

Jan. 1, 1667: did biber a good deal de vino. . . . Home to my chamber . . . and then to thinking upon establishing my vows against the next year.

Mar. 1: Vexed with Luce, our cook-mayde, who is a good drudging servant in everything else, and pleases us, but that she will be drunk and hath been so last night and all this day, that she could not make clean the house.

Mar. 26: I drank only burnt wine, as my whole custom of late hath been, as an evasion, God knows, for my drinking of wine (but it is an evasion which will not serve me now hot weather is coming, that I cannot pretend, as indeed I really have done, that I drank it for [a] cold), but I will leave it off.

(What with his elaborate drawing up of "vowes" not to drink, with due provision for their infraction every seventh day and their expiring before the holidays; what with his inventing of excuses to cover his indulgence, and his "aking" head and mental distress thereafter; his necessity for rereading his vows every "Lord's day," and his complete satisfaction when they hold fast,—life has become for Pepys such a complex problem that one feels it might have been almost simpler for him had he never begun to drink.)

Some of the most dreadful mischiefs proceed from wine; it is the cause of disease, quarrels, sedition, idleness, aversion to labor, and every species of domestic disorder.

—Fénelon (1651-1715).

In vain I trusted that the flowing bowl
Would banish sorrow, and enlarge the soul.
To the late revel, and protracted feast
Wild dreams succeeded, and disordered rest.
—Matthew Prior (1664-1721), *Solomon,* II.

Much drinking, little thinking.
—Swift (1667-1745), *Letter to Stella.*

Ever let my lovely pupils fear
To chill their mantling blood with cold small beer;
Destruction lurks within the poisonous dose,
A fatal fever or a pimpled nose.
—Soame Jenyns (1704-1787).

BENJAMIN FRANKLIN

(1706–1790)

At the head of Franklin's list of thirteen virtues which he tried to practice stood Temperance. On his admission as a young man to Watts' printing-house, London, he says:

I drank only water: the other workmen were great guzzlers of beer. On occasion, I carried up and down stairs a large form of types in each hand, when others carried but one in both hands. They wondered to see that the Water-American, as they called me, was *stronger* than themselves who drank *strong* beer. My companion at the press drank a pint before breakfast, a pint at breakfast, a pint between breakfast and dinner, a pint at dinner, a pint in the afternoon, and another when he had done his day's work.

I thought it a detestable custom; but it was necessary, he supposed, to drink *strong* beer, that he might be *strong* to labor. I endeavored to convince him that the bodily strength afforded by beer could only be in proportion to the grain or flour of which it is made; that there was more flour in a pennyworth of bread; and, therefore, if he would eat that with a pint of water, it would give him more strength than a pint of beer. He drank on, however, and had four or five shillings to pay out of his wages every Saturday night for that muddling liquor. And thus these poor devils keep themselves always under.

What you find fault with and clamour against, as the most terrible evil in the world, self-denial, is really the greatest good, and the highest self-gratification; if you use the word as understood by philosophers and men of sense, you will presently see her charms, and fly to her embraces, notwithstanding her demure looks, as absolutely necessary to produce even your own darling sole good, pleasure; for self-denial is never a reasonable action but as it is a natural means of procuring more pleasure than you can taste without it; so that this grave, saintlike guide to happiness is in truth the kindest and most beautiful mistress in the world.

All we have to do is to consider, when we passionately desire to enjoy a new object, whether gratifying that passion consists with our happiness tomorrow, next week, or next year; for, as we all wish to live, we are obliged by reason to take as much care for our future as our present happiness, and not build one upon the ruins of the other.

Natural or sensual pleasure continues no longer than the action itself; but divine or moral pleasure continues when the action is over and grows by reflection. If you enquire into the cause of the difference, and would know why the moral pleasures are greater than the sensual, perhaps the reason is the same as in all other creatures,—that their happiness or good consists in acting up to their chief faculty, that faculty which distinguishes them from all creatures of a different species.

Many a man thinks that he is buying pleasure, when he is really selling himself a slave to it. Pain wastes the body, pleasures the understanding. Nothing brings more pain than too much pleasure; nothing more bondage than too much liberty.

Wouldst thou enjoy a long life, a healthy body, and a vigorous mind, and be acquainted with the wonderful works of God, labor in the first place to bring thy appetite into subjection to reason.

It is no unprofitable pursuit to consider the manners and conversation of men who, insensible of the greatest enjoyment of humane life, abandon themselves to vice from a false notion of *pleasure* and good *fellow-ship*. A true representation of any enormity is often the best argument against it and means of removing it.

I would improve the little observation I have made on the vice of drunkenness, the better to reclaim the good fellows who usually pay the devotions of the evening to Bacchus.

It must be considered that no pleasure can give satisfaction or prove advantageous to a reasonable mind which is not attended with the restraints of reason. Enjoyment is not to be found in the excess of any sensual gratification; but on the contrary, the immoderate cravings of the voluptuary are always succeeded with loathing and a palled appetite. What pleasure can the drunkard have in the reflection that, while in his cups, he retained only the shape of a man, and acted the part of a beast; or that from reasonable discourse a few minutes before, he descended to impertinence and nonsense?

It argues some shame in the drunkards themselves, that they have invented numberless words to cover their folly whose proper significations are harmless. They are *boozy, tipsy, foxed, merry, mellow, fuddled,* etc.

Life with fools consists in drinking,
With the wise man, living's thinking.

When the wine enters, out goes the truth.

9

Drink does not drown care, but waters it and makes it grow faster.

Time eateth all things, could old poets say;
The times are changed, our times *drink* all away.

Experience keeps a dear school, yet fools will learn in no other.

What maintains one vice would bring up two children.

He that spills the Rum, loses that only;
He that drinks it, loses both that and himself.

Drunkenness, that worst of Evils,
Makes some men Fools, some Beasts, some Devils.

Against diseases here, the strongest Fence
Is the defensive Virtue, Abstinence.

Tomorrow you'll reform, you always cry;
In what far country does this morrow lie,
That 'tis so mighty long ere it arrive?
Beyond the Indies does this morrow live?
'Tis so far-fetched this morrow, that I fear
'Twill be both very old and very dear.
Tomorrow I'll reform, the fool does say;
Today itself's too late;—the wise did yesterday.

Each year one vicious habit rooted out,
In time might make the worst man good throughout.

DR. SAMUEL JOHNSON
(1709–1784)
(As reported by Boswell)

At one time a heavy drinker, Johnson, the supreme conversationalist, came to the conclusion that wine was an impediment to good conversation, and in 1757 described himself as "a hardened and shameless tea-drinker."

I supped with him at the Mitre tavern, that we might renew our social intimacy at the original place of meeting. But there was now a considerable difference in his way of living. Having had an illness, in which he was advised to leave off wine, he had continued to abstain from it, and drank only water or lemonade.

Finding him still persevering in his abstinence from wine, I ventured to speak to him of it. *Johnson:* "Sir, I found myself apt to go to excess in it, and therefore, having been for some time without it, on account of illness, I thought it better not to return to it." Lady MacLeod would hardly believe him (when later he told her this) and said, "I am sure, Sir, you would not carry it too far." "Nay, Madam, it carried *me*."

We discussed the question whether drinking improved conversation and benevolence. Sir Joshua maintained it did. *Johnson:* "No, Sir; before dinner men meet with great inequality of understanding; and those who are conscious of their inferiority have the modesty not to talk. When they have drunk wine every man feels himself happy, and loses that modesty, and grows impudent and vociferous: but he is not improved: he is only not sensible of his defects. (This is one of the disadvantages of wine,—it makes a man mistake words for thoughts.)

Sir Joshua said, "I am sure that moderate drinking makes people talk better." "No, Sir: wine gives not light, gay, ideal hilarity: but tumultuous, noisy, clamorous merriment. I have heard none of those *vinous* flights." *Sir Joshua:* "Because you have sat by quite sober, and felt an envy of the happiness of those who were drinking." *Johnson:* "Perhaps contempt. And, Sir, it is not necessary to be drunk oneself to relish the wit of drunkenness. Do we not judge of the drunken wit between Iago and Cassio, the most excellent of its kind, when we are quite sober? Wit, if good, will appear so at all times.

"I admit that the spirits are raised by drinking, as by the common participation of any pleasure: cockfighting or bearbaiting will raise the spirits of a company, as drinking does, though surely they will not improve the conversation. I also admit that there are some sluggish men who are improved by drinking; as there are fruits which are not good till they are rotten."

Dr. Johnson recommended to me often to drink water only: "For," said he, "you are then sure not to get drunk; whereas, if you drink wine, you are never sure." I said, drinking wine was a pleasure which I was unwilling to give up. "Why, Sir," said he, "there is no doubt that not to drink wine is a great deduction from life; but it may be necessary."

Boswell: "I think, Sir, you once said that not to drink wine was a great deduction from life." *Johnson:* "It is a diminution of pleasure, to be sure; but I do not say a diminution of happiness. There is more happiness in being rational." *Boswell:* "But if we could have pleasure always, should not we be happy? The greatest part of men would compound for pleasure." *Johnson:* "Supposing we could have pleasure always, an intellectual man would not compound for it. The greatest part of men would compound, because the greatest part of men are gross."

Boswell: "I allow there may be greater pleasure than from wine. I have had more pleasure from your conversation. I assure you I have." *Johnson:* "When we talk of pleasure, we mean sensual pleasure. When a man says he had pleasure with a woman, he does not mean conversation, but something of a different nature. Philosophers will tell you that pleasure is contrary to happiness. Gross men prefer animal pleasure. So there are men who have preferred living among savages. Now what a wretch must he be who is content with such conversation as can be had among savages!"

Next day, talking of a man's resolving to deny himself the use of wine from moral and religious considerations, he said: "He must not doubt about it. When one doubts as to pleasure, we know what will be the conclusion. I now no more think of drinking wine than a horse does. The wine upon the table is no more for me than for the dog who is under the table."

His profound reverence for the hierarchy made him expect from bishops the highest degree of decorum: he was offended even at their going into taverns: "A bishop," said he, "has nothing to do at a tippling house."

"A man," said he, "may choose whether he will have abstemiousness and knowledge, or claret and ignorance."

Said Mr. Burke, "Let me have claret: I love to have the careless gaiety of boyish days." *Johnson:* "I should drink claret too, if it would give me that; but it does not: it neither makes boys men, nor men boys."

"Wine makes a man better pleased with himself. But the danger is that while a man grows better pleased with himself, he may be growing less pleasing to others. Wine gives a man nothing. It neither gives him knowledge nor wit; it only animates a man and enables him to bring out what a dread of the company has repressed. It only puts in motion what has been locked up in frost. But this may be either good or bad." *Spottiswoode:* "So, Sir, wine is a key which opens a box; but this box may be either full or empty?" *Johnson:* "Nay, Sir, conversation is the key; wine is the pick-lock which forces open the box, and injures it. A man should cultivate his mind so as to have that confidence and readiness without wine which wine gives."

Boswell: "The great difficulty of resisting wine is from benevolence. For instance, a good worthy man asks you to taste his wine, which he has had twenty years in his cellar." *Johnson:* "Sir, all this notion about benevolence arises from a man's imagining himself to be of more importance to others than he really is. If they care this minute, they forget it the next. And as for the good worthy man, no good worthy man will insist upon another's drinking wine. Let us consider what a sad thing it would be if we were obliged to do anything else that may happen to be agreeable to the company where we are." *Langton:* "By the same rule you must join with a gang of cutpurses." *Johnson:* "Yes, Sir."

Boswell mentions a nobleman who, he believes, "was really uneasy if his company would not drink hard," and says: "Supposing I should be tête-à-tête with him at table?" *Johnson:* "Sir, there is no more reason for your drinking with *him* than his being sober with you." *Boswell:* "Why, that is true; for it would do him less hurt to be sober than it would do me to get drunk." *Johnson:* "Yes, Sir; and from what I have heard of him, one would not wish to sacrifice himself to such a man. If he must always have somebody drink with him, he should buy a slave, and then he would be sure to have it. They who submit to drink as another pleases make themselves his slaves." *Boswell:* "But, Sir, you will surely make allowance for the duty of hospitality. A gentleman who loves drinking comes to visit me." *Johnson:* "Sir, a man knows whom he visits; he comes to the table of a sober man."

(*In a letter to Boswell who was intending to become a candidate to represent York County in parliament*): "One thing I must enjoin you, which is seldom ob-

served in the conduct of elections; I must entreat you
to be scrupulous in the use of strong liquors. One
night's drunkenness may defeat the labors of forty days
well employed."

"In proportion as drinking makes a man different
from what he was before he has drunk, it is bad; because it has so far affected his reason."

—Dr. Johnson went to bed soon. When one bowl of
punch was finished, I rose, and was near the door, in
my way to bed; but Corrichatachin said it was the first
time Col had been in his house, and he should have
his bowl;—and would not I join in drinking it? The
heartiness of my honest landlord, and the desire of
doing social honour to our very obliging conductor,
induced me to sit down again. Col's bowl was finished;
and by that time we were well warmed. A third bowl
was soon made, and that too was finished. We were
cordial and merry to a degree; but of what passed I
have no recollection. A fourth bowl was made. I continued a little while with Corrie and Knockow; but
at last I left them. It was near five in the morning
when I got to bed.

I awaked at noon, with a severe headache. I was
much vexed, that I should have been guilty of such
a riot, and afraid of a reproof from Dr. Johnson. I
thought it very inconsistent with that conduct which
I ought to maintain, while the companion of the Ram-
bler. About one he came into my room, and accosted

me, "What, drunk yet?" His tone of voice was not
that of severe up-braiding; so I was relieved a little.
"Sir," said I, "they kept me up." He answered, "No,
you kept them up, you drunken dog."

When I rose, I went into Dr. Johnson's room, and
taking up Mrs. M'Kinnon's Prayer-book, I opened it
at the twentieth Sunday after Trinity, in the Epistle
for which I read, "Be not drunk with wine, wherein
is excess." Some would have taken this as divine
interposition.

At Grissipol we found a good farm-house belong-
ing to the Laird of Col. We were entertained with
primitive heartiness. Whiskey was served round in a
shell, according to the ancient Highland custom. Dr.
Johnson would not partake of it; but being desirous
to do honour to the modes "of other times," drank
some water out of the shell.

I will be lord over myself. Only he who masters
himself is worthy to rule, and only he can rule.

—Goethe (1749-1832).

When wine goes in, strange things come out.

—Schiller (1759-1805).

Call things by their right names. Glass of brandy
and water! That is the current but not the appropri-
ate name: ask for a glass of liquid fire and distilled
damnation.

—Robert Hall (1764-1831),
to a man who asked for a glass of brandy.

CHARLES LAMB
(1775–1834)

While still in his early manhood the lovable Charles Lamb, in what is perhaps his best-known poem, The Old Familiar Faces, *wrote:*

I have been laughing, I have been carousing,
Drinking late, sitting late, with my bosom cronies—

(*Strange that he could at that time already add:*)

All, all are gone, the old familiar faces.

Near the end of his life, in Confessions of a Drunkard, *the laughing has changed to sighing, the carousing to warning the unwary, and the dissolving of those early friendships is explained as typical of "all connections which have no solider fastenings than this liquid cement."*

Dehortations from the use of strong liquors have been the favorite topic of sober declaimers in all ages, and have been received with abundance of applause by water-drinking critics. But with the patient himself unfortunately their sound has seldom prevailed. Yet the evil is acknowledged, the remedy simple. Abstain. 'Tis as easy as not to steal, not to tell lies.

Alas! the hand to pilfer, and the tongue to bear false witness, have no constitutional tendency. Begin a reformation, and custom will make it easy. But what if the beginning be dreadful, and the first steps not like climbing a mountain, but going through fire? what if the whole system must undergo a change violent as that which we conceive of the mutation of form in some insects? what if a process comparable to flaying alive be to be gone through? Is the weakness that sinks under such struggles to be confounded with the pertinacity which clings to other vices which have induced no constitutional necessity, no engagement of the whole victim, body and soul?

I have known one in that state, when he has tried to abstain but for one evening,—though the poisonous potion had long since ceased to bring back its first enchantments, though he was sure it would rather deepen his gloom than brighten it,—in the violence of the struggle, and the necessity he had felt of getting rid of the present sensation at any rate, I have known him to scream out, to cry aloud, for the anguish and pain of the strife within him.

Why should I hesitate to declare that the man of whom I speak is myself? I have no puling apology to make to mankind. I see them in one way or another deviating from the pure reason. It is to my own nature alone that I am accountable for the woe that I have brought upon it.

I believe that there are constitutions, robust heads and iron insides, whom wine can do no worse injury to than just to muddle their faculties, perhaps never very pellucid. They would but laugh at a weak brother, who, trying his strength with them, and coming off foiled from the contest, would fain persuade them that such agonistic exercises are dangerous. It is to the weak—the nervous that I speak; to those who feel the want of some artificial aid to raise their spirits in society to what is no more than the ordinary pitch of all around them without it. Such must fly the convivial board in the first instance, if they do not mean to sell themselves for their term of life.

Twelve years ago I had completed my six and twentieth year. I had lived from the period of leaving school to that time pretty much in solitude. My companions were chiefly books, or at most one or two living ones of my own book-loving and sober stamp. I rose early, and went to bed betimes, and the faculties which God had given me, I have reason to think, did not rust in me unused.

About that time I fell in with some companions of a different order. They were men of boisterous spirits, sitters-up a-nights, disputants, drunken; yet they seemed to have something noble about them. We dealt about the wit, or what passes for it after midnight, jovially. Of the quality called fancy I certainly possessed a larger share than my companions. Encouraged by their applause, I set up for a professional joker.

Reader, if you are gifted with nerves like mine, aspire to any character but that of a wit. When you find a tickling relish upon your tongue disposing you to that sort of conversation, especially if you find a preternatural flow of ideas setting in upon you at the first sight of a bottle, avoid giving way to it as you would fly your greatest destruction. If you cannot crush the power of fancy, or that within you which you mistake for such, divert it, give it some other play.

To be an object of compassion to friends, of derision to foes; to be suspected by strangers, stared at by fools; to be esteemed dull when you cannot be witty; to be applauded for witty when you know that you have been dull; to swallow draughts of life-destroying wine which are to be distilled into airy breath to tickle vain auditors; to mortgage miserable mornings for nights of madness; to waste whole seas of time upon those who pay it back in little inconsiderate drops of grudging applause, are the wages of buffoonery and death.

Time, which has a sure stroke at dissolving all connections which have no solider fastenings than this liquid cement, more kind to me than my own taste or penetration, at length opened my eyes to the supposed qualities of my first friends. No trace of them is left but in the vices which they introduced, and the habits they infixed. In them my friends survive still and exercise ample retribution for any supposed infidelity that I may have been guilty of toward them.

My next more immediate companions were persons of such intrinsic and felt worth, that though accidentally their acquaintance has proved pernicious to me, I do not know that if the thing were to do over again, I should have the courage to eschew the mischief at the price of forfeiting the benefit.

They were no drinkers; but, one from professional habit, and another from a custom derived from his

father, smoked tobacco. The devil could not have devised a more subtle trap to re-take a backsliding peni-
tent. The transition, from gulping down draughts of
liquid fire to puffing out innocuous blasts of dry smoke,
was so like cheating him. But he beats us at a barter;
and when we think to set off a new failing against an
old infirmity, 'tis odds but he puts the trick upon us of
two for one.

It were impertinent to carry the reader through all
the processes by which, from smoking at first with malt
liquor, I took by degrees through thin wines, through
stronger wine and water, through small punch to those
juggling compositions which under the name of mixed
liquors, slur a great deal of brandy or other poison
under less and less water continually, until they come
to next to none, and so to none at all.

I should repel my readers were I to tell them what
tobacco has been to me, the drudging service I have
paid, the slavery I have vowed to it. How, when I
have resolved to quit it, a feeling as of ingratitude has
started up; how it has put on personal claims and made
the demands of a friend upon me. How the reading
of it casually in a book, as where Piscator in the *Complete Angler* breaks his fast upon a morning pipe, has
in a moment broken down the resistance of weeks. How
from illuminating it came to darken, from a quick
solace it turned to a negative relief, thence to a restless-
ness and dissatisfaction, thence to a positive misery.
How, even now, when the whole secret stands con-
fessed in all its dreadful truth before me, I feel myself

linked to it beyond the power of revocation. Bone of my bone—

Persons not accustomed to examine the motives of their actions, to reckon up the countless nails that rivet the chains of habit, may recoil from this as an over-charged picture. But what short of such a bondage is it, which in spite of protesting friends, a weeping wife and a reprobating world, chains down many a poor fellow, of no original indisposition to goodness, to his pipe and his pot?

I have seen a print after Correggio, in which three female figures are ministering to a man who sits bound at the root of a tree. Sensuality is soothing him, Evil Habit is nailing him to a branch, and Repugnance at the same instant is applying a snake to his side. When I saw this, I admired the wonderful skill of the painter. But when I went away I wept because I thought of my condition.

Of that there is no hope that it should ever change. The waters have gone over me. But out of the black depths, could I be heard, I would cry to all those who have but set a foot in the perilous flood. Could the youth, to whom the flavor of his first wine is delicious as the entering upon some newly-discovered paradise, look into my desolation, and be made to understand what a dreary thing it is when a man shall feel him-self going down a precipice with open eyes and a pas-sive will, to see his destruction and have no power to stop it, and yet to feel it emanating from himself; to perceive all goodness emptied out of him, and yet not be able to forget a time when it was otherwise; to bear about the piteous spectacle of his own self-ruin; could he see my fevered eye, feverish from last night's drinking, and feverishly looking for this night's repetition of the folly; could he feel the body of the death out of which I cry hourly with feebler and feebler outcry to be delivered, it were enough to make him dash the sparkling beverage to the earth in all the pride of its mantling temptation.

Yes, but (methinks I hear somebody object) if sobriety be that fine thing you would have us to understand, if the comforts of a cool brain are to be preferred to that state of heated excitement which you describe and deplore, what hinders that you do not return to those habits from which you would induce others never to swerve? If the blessing be worth preserving, is it not worth recovering?

Recovering!—O if a wish could transport me back to those days of youth, when a draught from the next clear spring could slake any heats which summer suns had power to stir up in the blood, how gladly would I return! But that which refreshes innocence only makes me sick and faint.

But is there no middle way between total abstinence and the excess which kills you?

For your sake, reader, and that you may never attain to my experience, with pain I must utter the dreadful truth, that there is none—none which I can find. In the stage of habit that I have reached, to stop short of that measure which is sufficient to draw on torpor and the benumbing apoplectic sleep of the drunkard, is to have taken none at all. The pain of self-denial is all one. And what that is, I had rather the reader should believe on my credit, than know from his own trial. He will come to know it, whenever he shall arrive at that state in which, paradoxical as it may appear, *reason shall only visit him through intoxication;* for it is a fearful truth, that the intellectual faculties by repeating acts of intemperance may be driven from their orderly sphere of action, their clear daylight ministries, until they shall be brought at last to depend, for the faint manifestation of their departing energies, upon the returning periods of the mental madness to which they owe their devastation.

Behold me, then, in the robust period of life, reduced to imbecility and decay. Twelve years ago I was possessed of a healthy frame of mind and body. Now, except when I am losing myself in a sea of drink, I am never free from those uneasy sensations in head and stomach, which are so much worse to bear than any definite pains or aches.

At that time I was seldom in bed after six in the morning. I awoke refreshed, and seldom without some merry thoughts or song to welcome the new-born day. Now, the first feeling which besets me is a forecast of the wearisome day that lies before me, with a secret wish that I could have lain on still, or never awaked.

My waking life has much of the confusion, the trouble, and obscure perplexity, of an ill dream. Busi-

ness wearies, affrights, perplexes me. The slightest
commission given me by a friend, or any small duty
which I have to perform, haunts me as a labor impossible to be got through. I dare not promise that a
friend's honor, or his cause, would be safe in my keeping. So much the springs of moral action are deadened
within me.

The noble passages which formerly delighted me in
history or poetic fiction now draw only a few tears,
allied to dotage. I perpetually catch myself in tears,
for any cause, or none. It is inexpressible how much
this infirmity adds to a sense of shame, and a general
feeling of deterioration.

I am a poor nameless egotist, who have no vanity
to consult by these Confessions. Such as they are, I
commend them to the reader's attention. I have told
him what I have come to, *Let him stop in time.*
                    —From *Confessions of a Drunkard.*

*It is heartbreaking that Lamb, who already had more
than one man's share of tragedy in his life, should have
drawn upon himself the added suffering and sense of
deterioration he so vividly portrays here. It was while
on his way to a tavern near Edmonton that he stumbled
against a stone and fell, and a few days later died at
the age of fifty-nine.*

Nothing can be more picturesque than an old grape-
vine, with almost a trunk of its own, clinging fast
around its supporting tree. Nor does the picture lack

its moral. The enemies of the vine might here have seen an emblem of the remorseless gripe which the habit of vinous enjoyment lays upon its victim, possessing him wholly, and letting him live no life but such as it bestows.

—Nathaniel Hawthorne (1804-1864),
The Marble Faun, chap. xxxii.

RALPH WALDO EMERSON
(1803–1882)

Genius is always ascetic. Appetite shows to finer souls as a disease, and they find beauty in rites and bounds that resist it.

We have found out fine names to cover our sensuality withal, but no gifts can raise intemperance. The man of talents affects to call his transgressions of the laws of the senses trivial, and to count them nothing considered with his devotion to his art. His art never taught him lewdness, nor the love of wine, nor the wish to reap where he had not sowed. His art is less for every deduction from his holiness, and less for every defect of common sense.

—*Prudence.*

A great number of such as were professionally expressers of Beauty, as painters, poets, musicians and actors, have been more than others wont to lead a life of pleasure and indulgence; all but the few who received the true nectar; and as it was a spurious mode of attaining freedom, as it was an emancipation not into the heavens but into the freedom of the baser places, they were punished for that advantage they won, by a dissipation and deterioration.

But never can any advantage be taken of nature by a trick. The spirit of the world, the great calm presence of the Creator, comes not forth to the sorceries of opium or of wine. The sublime vision comes to the pure and simple soul in a clean and chaste body. That is not an inspiration which we owe to narcotics, but some counterfeit excitement and fury. He who shall sing of the gods and their descent unto men, must drink water out of a wooden bowl. For poetry is not "Devil's wine," but God's wine.

—The Poet.

The brave soul rates itself too high to value itself by the splendor of its table and draperies. It gives what it hath, and all it hath, but its own majesty can lend a better grace to bannocks and fair water than belongs to city feasts.

The temperance of the hero proceeds from the same wish to do no dishonor to the worthiness he has. But he loves it for its elegancy, not for its austerity.

—Heroism.

You remember the story of the poor woman who importuned Philip of Macedon to grant her justice, which Philip refused: the woman exclaimed, "I appeal": the king, astonished, asked to whom she appealed: the woman replied, "From Philip drunk to Philip sober."

—New England Reformers.

There is this to be said in favor of drinking, that it takes the drunkard first out of society, then out of the world.

—*Journal,* 1866.

I am glad to have drunk water so long, for the same reason that I prefer the natural sky to an opium-eater's heaven. I would fain keep sober always; and there are infinite degrees of drunkenness. I believe that water is the only drink for a wise man; wine is not so noble a liquor.

—Henry David Thoreau (1817-1862), *Walden.*

Avant la révolution, quand un grand personnage traversait une ville de Bourgogne ou de Champagne, le corps de ville lui présentait quatre gondoles d'argent dans lesquelles on avait versé quatre vins différents. Sur le premier gobelet on lisait cette inscription: *vin de singe:* sur le deuxième, *vin de lion:* sur le troisième, *vin de mouton;* sur le quatrième, *vin de cochon.* Ces quatre légendes exprimaient les quatre degrés que descend l'ivrogne; la première ivresse, celle qui égaye; la deuxième, celle qui irrite; la troisième, celle qui hébète; la dernière enfin, celle qui abrutit.

—Victor Hugo (1802-1885), *Les Misérables,*
Cosette VI, 9.

Indeed the Idols I have loved so long
Have done my credit in the World much wrong:
Have drown'd my Glory in a shallow Cup,
And sold my reputation for a Song.

—Edward Fitzgerald (1809-1883),
Omar Khayyám.

Since the creation of the world there has been no tyrant like Intemperance, and no slaves so cruelly treated as his.

—William Lloyd Garrison, (1805-1879).

CHARLES DICKENS
(1812–1870)

Didn't you ever go to school, Joe, when you were as little as me?

No, Pip.

Why?

Well, Pip, I'll tell you. My father, Pip, he were given to drink, and when he were overtook with drink, he hammered away at my mother most onmerciful. It were a'most the only hammering he did, indeed, 'xcepting at myself. And he hammered at me with a wigor only to be equalled by the wigor with which he didn't hammer at his anwil. Consequence, my mother and me run away from my father several times; and then my mother she'd go out to work, and she'd say, "Joe, now, please God, you shall have some schooling, child," and she'd put me to school. But my father were that good in his hart that he couldn't bear to be without us. So he'd come with a most tremenjous crowd and make such a row at the doors of the houses where we was, that they used to be obligated to have no more to do with us and to give us up to him. And then he took us home and hammered us. Which you see, Pip, were a drawback on my learning. Though mind you, Pip, rendering unto all their doo, and maintaining equal justice between man and man, my father were that good in his hart, don't you see?

(I didn't see; but I didn't say so.)

Well! Joe pursued, somebody must keep the pot a-biling, Pip, or the pot won't bile, don't you know? Consequence, my father didn't make no objections to my going to work; so I went at my present calling which were his too, if he would have followed it, and in time I were able to keep him, and I kep' him till he went off in a purple 'leptic fit.

—*Great Expectations,* Chap. VII.

THOMAS HUXLEY

(1825–1895)

Extracts from his Letters

Oct. 22, 1854: I feel I am in for a life-long dyspeps. I have not now nervous energy enough for stomach and brain both, and if I work the latter, not even the fresh breezes of this place will keep the former in order.

May 6, 1862: I have amused myself by spending ten days or so in bed. I had an unaccountable prostration of strength which I believe was nothing but an obstruction of the liver. Of course I can't persuade people of this, and they will have it that it is overwork. I have come to the conviction, however, that steady work hurts nobody, the real destroyer of hardworking men being not their work, but dinners, late hours and the universal humbug of society.

Sept. 9, 1872: I have been worried to death with dyspepsia and the hypochondriacal bewilderments that follow in its train.

Sept. 17, 1872: My stay was marred by continuous dyspepsia and concurrent hypochondriacal incapacity. By dint of living on cocoa and Revalenta, and giving up drink, tobacco, . . . I am getting better.

Oct. 16, 1873: My dear Rolleston: A note from Mrs. Rolleston to my wife the other day gave us a poor account of your health. Is it dyspeps again? If so, follow in my steps. I mean to go about the country, with somebody who can lecture, as the "horrid example"—cured. Nothing but gross and disgusting intemperance, Sir, was the cause of all my evil. Now that I have been a teetotaler for nine months, and have cut down my food supply to about half of what I used to eat, the enemy is beaten. As this is the third letter I have written before breakfast (a thing I never could achieve when I wallowed in the sty of Epicurus), you perceive that I am as vigorous as ever I was in my life.

April 9, 1889: Dear Sir: I understand that you ask me what I think about "alcohol as a stimulant to the brain in mental work?"

Speaking for myself (and perhaps I may add for persons of my temperament), I can say, without hesitation, that I would just as soon take a dose of arsenic as I would of alcohol, under such circumstances. Indeed, on the whole, I should think the arsenic safer, less likely to lead to physical and moral degradation. It would be better to die outright than to be alcoholized before death. If a man cannot do brain work without stimulants of any kind, he had better turn to hand work—it is an indication on Nature's part that she did not mean him to be a head worker.*

EMILE ZOLA

(1840–1902)

Extracts from Émile Zola's novel, L'Assommoir (The Saloon), *that epic of the inebriate, which paints with terrible realism the ravages wrought in the life of the Parisian workingman by his great enemy, liquor; the alcoholic brutality which Bijard wreaks on his wife and innocent child, and the successive stages of degradation through which the zinc worker Coupeau, his wife Gervaise, and young daughter Nana descend from contented respectability to debauchery and death.*

When she reached home, Gervaise found the whole tenement in an uproar.

"It's Père Bijard beating his wife. He was downstairs raging drunk waiting for her to get back from the laundry; he drove her upstairs with his two fists and now he's bludgeoning her up there. Listen, don't you hear her screams?"

Life and Letters of Thomas Huxley, by Leonard Huxley. Copyright, 1900, by D. Appleton & Co.

Gervaise flew upstairs. She was very fond of Madame Bijard, she was such a courageous woman. Above, the door of the room was wide open, and some of the tenants were ejaculating on the landing while Madame Boche, standing at the door, cried:

"Will you stop! They're going to call the police, do you hear?"

No one dared to enter the room because Bijard was like a wild beast when he was drunk. Moreover, he was rarely sober; and on the few days that he worked he used to set a bottle of brandy near his locksmith's vise and take a pull at it every now and then. He would have caught fire like a torch if a match had been brought anywhere near his mouth.

"But we can't let her be murdered!" cried Gervaise, trembling all over. And she went in. The room was bare and cold, for the man had sold the very sheets off the bed to satisfy his passion for drink. In the fray, the table had been upset and the two chairs were upside down. On the floor Madame Bijard, her hair streaming over her bloody face, groaned horribly at every blow Bijard gave her. First he had pounded her with his fists, now he was kicking her.

"You wench! You wench!" he growled in smothered tones, accompanying every word with a blow, and hitting the harder the more he choked. The face framed in the stained beard was livid, the bald forehead spotted with great red blotches.

Meanwhile Père Bru had followed Gervaise into the room. They tried to reason with the locksmith, to push him toward the door. But he turned on them foaming at the mouth, and in his pale eyes the alcohol burned, a murderous flame. Gervaise had her hand crushed, old Père Bru fell over the table. On the floor Madame Bijard breathed more heavily, her mouth wide open, her eyes closed. Now Bijard missed her; but he returned to the attack, fuming, struck this way and that, blind and enraged, hitting himself or the empty air. And during all this violence Gervaise saw in a corner of the room little Lalie watching her father attack her mother. She was standing up, very pale and serious, holding her arms around her little sister Henriette to protect her. Her large dark eyes were fixed in a pensive stare.

Several years later the foul work was finished:

With tears in her eyes Gervaise told how Madame Bijard had died that very morning after suffering untold agony.

"It came from a kick Bijard gave her. No doubt it caused an internal injury. Ah, mon Dieu, there's many a scoundrel in the galleys now who's not so bad as him. But the law would have too much to do if it bothered about all the wives pounded to death by their men. One kick more or less, that doesn't matter, does it, when they're getting them every day. Especially as the poor woman tried to save her man from the scaffold and so explained that she had injured herself falling over a tub. She cried out all night before she went. Only two weeks ago she weaned her last baby, little Jules, which was lucky, because now he won't suffer. Still, there's that little Lalie left to care for those two mites. She's not eight years old. And then, too, her father beats her unmercifully. Ah well! some people seem born to suffer!"

Little Lalie ran the household just like an older person; and the work was heavy. She had to watch over the two little ones of three and five years all day while she was sweeping and washing the dishes. Without a word, she slipped into the place of her dead mother, even to the point of being beaten by that brute of a father just as her mother had been. When he came home drunk, he had to have a woman to torture.

In the Coupeau household also alcohol was beginning to take its toll. To keep going now Coupeau had to have his daily measure of brandy; it was his food and his drink, the only thing he could digest.

One Saturday Gervaise having gone to look for her husband in Père Colombe's saloon, she is herself drawn into drinking with the men, till, after the third drink,

the room danced, the gas jets twinkled like stars. Gervaise was drunk. Then, suddenly there was a commotion followed by outcries and the noise of tables overturned. It was Père Colombe driving the company outdoors without ceremony. Gervaise lost Coupeau, found him again, and lost him once more. She wanted to go home, held onto the walls so as not to lose her way. At the corner of rue des Poissonniers

From the drawing by Gavarni   Courtesy of Walters Art Gallery, Baltimore

she sat down in the gutter. At last she arrived; she stumbled past the concierge's door and could see the expression of disgust on the faces of the Lorilleux and the Poissons sitting there at the table. How she got up the six flights of stairs she didn't know; but once in the corridor, little Lalie who heard her ran out, laughing and saying: "Madame Gervaise, papa hasn't come home yet: so come see my children asleep. My, but they're cute!" Then, seeing the stupified face of the woman, she shrank back trembling. She knew only too well this brandied breath, the pale eyes and twitching mouth. Then Gervaise blundered by without a word, while the little girl, silent and grave, followed her with her deep gaze.

Another Saturday, Nana coming in found her father and mother in a deplorable state. Coupeau had fallen across the bed and was snoring. Gervaise, slumped on a chair, was rolling her head from side to side, her vague disquieting eyes staring at vacancy. She had forgotten to heat up the dinner. An untrimmed candle cast a dismal light over the wretched lodging.

"Is that you, girl?" stuttered Gervaise. "Well, your father's going to settle with you!"

Nana didn't answer: she stood white as a sheet, looked at the cold stove, the unset table, the room whose sordidness was heightened by the condition of this pair of sots. She didn't take off her hat, but with clenched teeth she opened the door and went out. And she didn't come back.

Gervaise, furious, gave herself up to a three-day orgy, her fists clinched and uttering a stream of horrible threats against her daughter. Coupeau, after having roamed about the boulevards and peered into the faces of the bundles of rags that passed by, began to smoke his pipe once more; only, when he was at the table he would get up sometimes, wave his arms, a knife in one fist, and cry out that he was dishonored.

Gervaise fell lower still; she used to beg a charitable restaurant-keeper for the crusts his clients left. She would arrive, the days she was doubled up with hunger, to prowl with the dogs around the doors of the shops before the garbage collectors had passed; and in that way she sometimes got a rotten melon, a spoiled fish or cutlets from which she would brush the vermin with her sleeves. Yes, it had come to that!

She was slumping heavily along the corridor one day, her shoulders bent, when arriving before the door of the Bijards' room she heard low moans; she went in.

The room was very neat. You could see that Lalie that very morning had swept and put it in order. The two little children had found some old pictures that they were quietly cutting up in a corner. But Gervaise was surprised to see Lalie lying on her narrow folding bed, very pale. She raised her white lids and tried to smile, but there was a convulsive shudder of her lips instead. Then, closing her eyes again, she said with an effort; "I've been so tired these days that I'm coddling myself, you see."

But the childish face, covered with livid blotches, took on an expression of such supreme agony that Gervaise, forgetting her own woes, clasped her hands and fell on her knees beside her. For a whole month she had noticed her holding on to the walls in order to walk, bent double by an ominous cough. Now she could only hiccough, and there were little trickles of blood from the corners of her mouth.

"I dragged myself around and put things to rights a bit. It is neat, isn't it? I wanted to wash the windows, but my legs went from under me. Silly, wasn't it? Well, when you can't do anything more, you lie down.— Please look and see that my children aren't cutting themselves with the scissors." And she stopped, trembling, hearing a heavy step on the stair. Brutally, Père Bijard pushed open the door. As usual he was lit up, his eyes blazing with a fury kindled by liquor. When he saw Lalie in bed, he took down a long whip, growling:

"Ah, nom de Dieu, this is too much! So the cows go to bed at midday now!" He was already cracking the whip above the bed when the child said pleadingly:

"No, papa, please don't. I know you'll be sorry if you do."

"Are you going to get up?" he growled louder still. "I'll tickle your sides!"

But she said softly, "I can't, don't you see? I'm dying."

Bijard, aghast, stood still before the cot. What kind of tale was that? Do they die as young as that without first being ill?

"You'll see, it's so," she continued. "Be good and tell me good-bye, papa."

Bijard's face twitched. It was true she had a little long face as serious as a grown-up's. The presence of Death in the narrow chamber suddenly sobered him. He took a look about the room like a man awakened from a long sleep, saw everything was in order and the two children playing and laughing in a corner. And he plumped down on a chair, stammering; "Our little mother, our little mother!"

On the dark, wide sidewalk when the gaiety of the neighboring avenues was dying down, women were silently waiting. They would stay for some time motionless; then, slowly, they would take ten steps and stop once more. Gervaise tried to do as they did. Men passed without turning the head. Then she tried moving; she dared to accost a man who was whistling and murmured in smothered tones,

"Sir, please listen!"

The man gave her a glance and went on his way whistling more loudly. She was furious and changed her place, went to the rue de la Chapelle.

"Sir, please listen!"

But the men passed by

On Sunday Gervaise received a note telling her that her poor sot was in a fair way to die at St. Anne's Asylum. It seems that Coupeau had been fished up out of the river at the Pont Neuf; he had thrown himself over the parapet thinking he saw a bearded man who barred the way.

Gervaise was in no hurry to go; however Monday she left at noon and had to cross the whole city. At last she arrived. An orderly took her up. As she mounted the stairs she heard howls which sent a shiver through her very bones.

"Beautiful music he's making, eh?" said the orderly.

"Who is?"

"Why, your man! He's been howling like that since the day before yesterday, and he dances, you'll see!"

Ah, mon Dieu! What a sight! She stood stock still. The cell was padded from floor to ceiling; on the floor two straw mats, one on the other; and, in a corner a mattress, with a bolster; nothing more. In the cell Coupeau danced and howled, his blouse in shreds, his limbs beating the air. He would bump against the window, recoil, beating a measure with his arms; shake his hands as if he wanted to break them off and hurl them at the face of the world. You see buffoons in night clubs doing that, but you'd have to watch this drunkard's rigadoon to see what *chic* it takes on when danced in dead earnest. The accompanying song had its peculiar character too,—a sort of continuous scolding, the mouth wide open emitting for hours on end the same raucous trombone notes. It was the cry of a dog whose paw has been crushed. Was it possible that he could look like that, blood in his eyes and his lips crusted over? She surely wouldn't have known him. His skin looked varnished and was reeking with perspiration. He clenched his fists, then running, fell flat, and, his teeth chattering with terror, stammered, "They're trying to kill me. No, I won't throw myself over, I won't!"

AN ADAGE FROM THE ORIENT

At the punch-bowl's brink
Let the thirsty think
What they say in Japan.
"First the man takes a drink,
Then the drink takes a drink,
Then the drink takes the man."
—Edward Rowland Sill (1841-1887).

I have better use for my brain than to poison it with alcohol. To put alcohol in the human brain is like putting sand in the bearings of an engine.
—Thomas A. Edison (1847-1931).

OSCAR WILDE

(1856–1900)

Oscar Wilde was fully conscious of the close relation between alcohol and crime: the prisoner in the Ballad of Reading Gaol

did not wear his scarlet coat,
For blood and wine are red,

And blood and wine were on his hands
When they found him with the dead,
The poor dead woman whom he loved,
And murdered in her bed.

HÉLAS!

To drift with every passion till my soul
Is a stringed lute on which all winds can play,
Is it for this that I have given away
Mine ancient wisdom, and austere control?
Methinks my life is a twice-written scroll
Scrawled over on some boyish holiday
With idle songs for pipe and virelay,
Which do but mar the secret of the whole.
Surely there was a time I might have trod
The sunlit heights, and from life's dissonance
Struck one clear chord to reach the ears of God:
Is that time dead?......................
And must I lose a soul's inheritance?

We drink one another's healths and spoil our own.
   —Jerome K. Jerome (1859-1927),
      On Eating and Drinking.

The water wagon is the place for me!
Last night my feelings were immense;
Today I feel like thirty cents!
No time for mirth, no time for laughter—
The cold gray dawn of the morning after.
   —George Ade (1866-1944), *Remorse,*
     from *The Sultan of Sulu.*

There are two times when you can never tell what
is going to happen. One is when a man takes his first
drink: and the other is when a woman takes her latest.
—O. Henry (1867-1910), *The Gentle Grafter*.

BLASCO IBAÑEZ

(1867–1928)

Spain was the land of wine, and Salvatierra cursed
the power that alcoholic poison wielded over the
people, transmitting its evil from generation to generation. The wine-warehouse was the modern counterpart of the feudal fortress that held the masses in
slavery and abjection. Their enthusiasm, their crimes,
their joys, their love—were all the product of wine.

Salvatierra spoke of wine as of an invisible, all-
powerful personage, who intervened in all the deeds
of these automatons, suggesting their very thoughts, as
limited and capricious as those of a bird, plunging
them into despair as well as into disorderd happiness.

Intelligent men who could serve as leaders for those
below them revealed generous aspirations in their
youth, but scarcely did they become of age when they
fell victims to the epidemic of the land: they were
converted into renowned "wine-growers," and their
brains were unable to function unless stimulated by
alcohol. In the very prime of life they became de-
crepit, with trembling hands—almost paralytic—red
eyes, obscured sight and confused thoughts; as if the
fumes of the alcohol had shrouded their minds in
clouds.

"Wine!" exclaimed Salvatierra. "That is the chief enemy of this country: it destroys our energy, it creates false hopes, it brings immature old age; it ruins everything—even love."

—La Bodega.

E. P. Dutton & Co. Inc., publisher.*

JOHN MASEFIELD
(1878–   )

In the course of his early wanderings Masefield once worked in a saloon. The experience is vividly reflected in *The Everlasting Mercy,* a small portion of which follows: †

> From '51 to '61
> I cut my teeth and took to fun . . .
> I learned with what a rosy feeling
> Good ale makes floors seem like the ceiling,
> And how the moon gives shiny light
> To lads as roll home singing by't.
> My blood did leap, my flesh did revel,
> Saul Kane was tokened to the devil.

> From '61 to '67
> I lived in disbelief of Heaven.
> I drunk, I fought, I poached, I whored,
> I did despite unto the Lord.

I cursed, 'twould make a man look pale,
And nineteen times I went to gaol. . . .

Each one could be a Jesus mild,
Each one has been a little child,
A little child with laughing look,
A lovely white unwritten book;
A book that God will take, my friend,
As each goes out at journey's end.
The Lord who gave us Earth and Heaven
Takes that as thanks for all He's given.
The book He lent is given back
All blotted red and smutted black. . . .

The room was full of men and stink
Of bad cigars and heavy drink.
Riley was nodding to the floor
And gurgling as he wanted more.
His mouth was wide, his face was pale,
His swollen face was sweating ale;
And one of those assembled Greeks
Had corked black crosses on his cheeks.
Thomas was having words with Goss,
He "wouldn't pay, the fight was cross."
And Goss told Tom that "cross or no,
The bets go as the verdicts go,
By all I've ever heard or read of.
So pay, or else I'll knock your head off."
Jim Gurvil said his smutty say
About a girl down Bye Street way. . . .

What with the fight and what with drinking
And being awake alone there thinking,
My mind began to carp and tetter,
"If this life's all, the beasts are better." . . .
I wondered, then, why life should be,
And what would be the end of me
When youth and health and strength were gone
And cold old age came creeping on? . . .
And looking round I felt disgust
At all the nights of drink and lust,
And all the looks of all the swine
Who'd said that they were friends of mine. . . .

There used to be a custom then,
Miss Bourne, the Friend, went round at ten
To all the pubs in all the place,
To bring the drunkards' souls to grace;
Some sulked, of course, and some were stirred,
But none give her a dirty word. . . .

"Saul Kane," she said, "when next you drink,
Do me the gentleness to think
That every drop of drink accursed
Makes Christ within you die of thirst,
That every dirty word you say
Is one more flint upon His way,
Another thorn about His head,
Another mock by where He tread,
Another nail, another cross.
All that you are is that Christ's loss. . . .

And "Tick. Slow. Tick. Slow" went the clock.
She said, "He waits until you knock." . . .

I know the very words I said,
They bayed like bloodhounds in my head.
"The water's going out to sea
And there's a great moon calling me;
But there's a great sun calls the moon,
And all God's bells will carol soon
For joy and glory and delight
Of someone coming home tonight." . . .

I did not think, I did not strive,
The deep peace burnt my me alive;
The bolted door had broken in,
I knew that I had done with sin.
I knew that Christ had given me birth
To brother all the souls on earth. . . .

O glory of the lighted mind.
How dead I'd been, how dumb, how blind.
The station brook, to my new eyes,
Was babbling out of Paradise,
The waters rushing from the rain
Were singing Christ has risen again.
I thought all earthly creatures knelt
From rapture of the joy I felt. . . .

It's dawn, and I must wander north
Along the road Christ led me forth.

The liquor traffic is sacrilege, for it seeks profit from
the damnation of human souls.
                    —Harry Emerson Fosdick (1878-   ).

"JACK" LONDON

(1876–1916)

First an oyster pirate, then a member of the fish patrol, at seventeen he signed as seaman on a sealing vessel. He joined the first gold rush to the Klondike, was a war correspondent in Japan, attempted a cruise around the world in a small yacht. Novelist and socialist, perhaps The Call of the Wild *and* The Iron Heel *are the most popular of his works. The following excerpts are from his semi-autobiographical novel,* John Barleycorn.*

We were three tipsy young gods, incredibly wise, gloriously genial, and without any limit to our powers. Ah! could John Barleycorn keep one at such a height, I should never draw a sober breath again. But this is not a world of free freights. One pays according to an iron schedule—for every strength the balanced weakness; for every high a corresponding low; for every fictitious godlike moment an equivalent time in reptilian slime. We pay for every nerve Marathon we run. John Barleycorn can lead us to the heights, but he cannot keep us there. And there is no devotee but pays for the mad dances John Barleycorn pipes.

Scotty strove to take another drink, and feebly dropped the tumbler to the floor. Then, to my amaze-

* From: *John Barleycorn* by Jack London. Copyright, 1913, Century Company. Reprinted by permission of Appleton-Century-Crofts, Inc.

ment, weeping bitterly, he rolled into a bunk and immediately snored off to sleep. Then the harpooner faded away into his bunk, and I was left alone, unthrown, on the field of battle. I was very proud. I could carry my drink. I was a man. I had drunk two men, drink for drink, into unconsciousness. And I was still on my two feet, making my way on deck to get air into my scorching lungs.

It was on this bout on the *Idler* that I discovered what a good stomach and a strong head I had for drink—a bit of knowledge that was to be a source of pride in succeeding years, and that ultimately I was to come to consider a great affliction. The fortunate man is the one who cannot take more than a couple of drinks without becoming intoxicated. The unfortunate wight is the one who can take many glasses without betraying a sign; who *must* take numerous glasses in order to get the "kick."

They couldn't wait a moment to celebrate the fifty dollars they had so easily earned. It is the way of the devotees of John Barleycorn. When good fortune comes, they drink. When they have no fortune they drink to the hope of good fortune. If fortune be ill, they drink to forget it. If they meet a friend, they drink. If they quarrel with a friend and lose him, they drink. If their love-making be crowned with success, they are so happy they must needs drink. If they be jilted, they drink for the contrary reason. If they haven't anything to do, why they take a drink. When they are sober they want to drink; and when they have drunk they want to drink more.

At one o'clock in the morning, after a prodigious drunk, I was tottering aboard a sloop when I tumbled overboard. And then John Barleycorn played me his maniacal trick. Some maundering fancy of going out with the tide suddenly obsessed me. Thoughts of suicide had never entered my head. And now that they entered, I thought it fine, a splendid culmination, a perfect rounding off of my short but exciting career. And in passing, let me note that this maniacal trick John Barleycorn played me is nothing uncommon. An absolute statistic of the percentage of suicides due to John Barleycorn would be appalling.*

And here is another complaint I bring against John Barleycorn. It is the good fellows (easy and genial, daring, and, on occasion, mad) that he gets—the fellows with the fire and the go in them, who have bigness, and warmness, and the best of the human weaknesses. And John Barleycorn puts out the fire, and soddens the agility, and, when he does not more immediately kill them or make maniacs of them, he coarsens and grossens them, and twists and malforms them out of the original goodness and fineness of their natures.

---

* On the morning of Nov. 22, 1916, "Jack" London's Japanese servant found him unconscious, on the floor two vials labeled poisons. So died this doughty adventurer when only forty years of age.

And the reason why these best are destroyed is because John Barleycorn stands on every highway and byway, accessible, law-protected, saluted by the policeman on the beat, speaking to them, leading them by the hand to the places where the good fellows and daring ones foregather and drink deep. With John Barleycorn out of the way, these daring ones would do things instead of perishing.

Back in Oakland from my wanderings, I drank every day, and whenever opportunity offered I drank to excess. I was learning what it was to have no appetite. I was learning what it was to get up shaky in the morning, with a stomach that quivered, with fingers touched with palsy, and to know the drinker's need for a stiff glass of whisky in order to brace up. (Oh! John Barleycorn is a wizard dopester. Brain and body, scorched and jangled and poisoned, return to be tuned up by the very poison that caused the damage.)

I learned that there were limits to my gorgeous constitution, that in a short hour or two John Barleycorn could master my strong head, put me on my back, and with a devil's grip on my throat proceed to choke the life out of me.

John Barleycorn, by inhibiting morality, incited to crime. Saloon-mates I drank with, who were good fellows and harmless, sober, did most violent and lunatic things when drunk. And then the police gathered them in and they vanished from our ken. Sometimes I visited them behind the bars and said good-by ere they journeyed across the bay to put on the felon's stripes. And time and again I heard: *If I hadn't been drunk I wouldn't a-done it.* And sometimes, under the spell of John Barleycorn, the most frightful things were done—things that shocked even my case-hardened soul.

The habitual drunkards had a way of turning up their toes without apparent provocation. When they took sick, even with trifling afflictions that any ordinary man could pull through, they just pegged out. Sometimes they were found dead in their beds; on occasion their bodies were dragged out of the water; and sometimes it was just plain accident.

One who has been burned by fire must preach about the fire. I was just human, and I was taking the path that men took whom I admired; full-blooded men, lusty, free spirits and anything but niggards in the way they foamed life away.

And the way was open. It was like an uncovered well in a yard where children play. It is small use to tell the brave little boys that they mustn't play near the well. They *will* play near it. And we know that a certain percentage of them, the livest and most daring, will fall into the well. The case is the same with John Barleycorn. All the no-saying and no-preaching in the world will fail to keep men, and youths growing into manhood, away from John Barleycorn when he is everywhere accessible, and is everywhere the connotation of manliness, and daring, and great-spiritedness. The only rational thing to do is to cover up the well, and to relegate to the nineteenth century and all the preceding centuries the witch-burnings, the intolerances, the fetiches, and, not least among such barbarisms, John Barleycorn.

When I turned in my last examination paper I was in full possession of a splendid case of brain-fag. More than anything else in the world, my frayed and frazzled mind wanted surcease from weariness in the way it knew surcease would come. For the first time in my life I consciously, deliberately desired to get drunk. It was not a body need for alcohol. My overworked and jaded mind wanted to forget. Granted my prodigious brain-fag, nevertheless, had I never drunk in the past, the thought would never have entered my mind to get drunk now. Beginning with drinking only for the sake of comradeship and because alcohol was everywhere on the adventure-path, I had now reached the stage where my brain cried out, not merely for a drink, but for a drunk.

John Barleycorn makes his appeal to weakness and failure, to weariness and exhaustion. He is the easy way out. He offers strength to the body, false elevation to the spirit, making things seem vastly fairer than they are. But it must not be forgotten that John Barleycorn is protean. As well as to weakness and exhaustion, does he appeal to superabundant vitality, to the ennui of idleness. He can tuck in his arm the arm of any man in any mood. He exchanges new lamps for old, the spangles of illusion for the drabs of reality, and in the end cheats all who traffic with him.

And now we begin to come to it. A cocktail * or two, before dinner, enabled me to laugh whole-heartedly at things which had long ceased being laughable. I achieved a false exhilaration, drugged myself to merriment. But the same stimulus to the human organism will not continue to produce the same response. By and by I discovered there was no kick at all in one cocktail. Two or three were required to produce the original effect of one. And I wanted that effect. I drank my first cocktail at eleven-thirty and two or more cocktails before I ate. This became schedule—three cocktails in the hour that intervened between my desk and dinner. And these were two of the deadliest drinking habits: regular drinking and solitary drinking.

The time came when the cocktails were inadequate. Whisky had a more powerful jolt. I had been accustomed to read myself to sleep when I chanced to awake. Now this began to fail me. I found that a drink furnished the soporific effect. Sometimes two or three drinks were required. If I traveled to out-of-way places, I took a quart, or several quarts, along in my grip. In the past I had been amazed by other men guilty of this practice. Now I did it myself unblushingly. I was carrying a beautiful alcoholic conflagration around with me. There was no time, in all my waking time, that I didn't want a drink. I began to

---

* The name derives not inappropriately from a large beetle known as the Devil's coach-horse; also called *cocktail* from its habit of cocking up the long jointed abdomen when irritated.

anticipate the completion of my daily thousand words by taking a drink when only five hundred were written. It was not long until I prefaced the beginning of the thousand words with a drink.

I made new rules. Resolutely I would refrain from drinking until my work was done. But a new complication arose. The work refused to be done without drinking. I had to drink in order to do it. I was beginning to fight now. I had the craving at last, and it was mastering me. I would sit at my desk and dally with pad and pen, but the words refused to flow.

And like a survivor of old red War who cries out, "Let there be no more war!" so I cry out, "Let there be no more poison-fighting by our youths!" The way China stopped the general use of opium was by stopping the cultivation and importation of opium. The philosophers, priests and doctors of China could have preached themselves breathless against opium for a thousand years, and the use of opium, so long as opium was ever-accessible, would have continued unabated. We have made a practice of not leaving arsenic and strychnine, and typhoid and tuberculosis germs lying around for our children to be destroyed by. Treat John Barleycorn the same way. Stop him. Don't let him lie around, licensed and legal, to pounce upon our youth. Not for alcoholics, it is the healthy, normal boys for whom I write.

And it will be easy. The only ones that will be hurt will be the topers and seasoned drinkers of a single generation. I am one of these, and I make solemn

assurance, based upon long traffic with John Barleycorn, that it won't hurt me very much to stop drinking when no drink is obtainable. On the other hand,
the overwhelming proportion of young men are so
normally non-alcoholic, that, never having had access
to alcohol, they will never miss it. They will think of
the saloon as a quaint old custom similar to bull bait-
ing and the burning of witches.

Not one drinker in a million began drinking alone.
All drinkers begin socially, and this drinking is accom-
panied by a thousand social connotations. The human
is rarely born who, without long training in the social
relations of drinking, feels the irresistible propulsion of
his system toward alcohol.

LIQUOR FROM A TO Z

THE LIQUOR EVIL

*A*rms more villains,
*B*reaks more laws,
*C*orrupts more officials,
*D*estroys more homes,
*E*ngulfs more fortunes,
*F*ills more jails,
*G*rows more gray hairs,
*H*arrows more hearts,
*I*ncites more crime,
*J*eopardizes more lives,
*K*indles more strife,
*L*acerates more feelings,
*M*aims more bodies,
*N*ails down more coffins,
*O*pens more graves,
*P*laces more feet on the downward path,
*Q*uenches more hopes,
*R*aises more sobs,
*S*ells more virtue,
*T*ells more lies,
*U*ndermines more youth,
*V*oids more contracts,
*W*recks more men,
*X*cites more murders,
*Y*ields more disgrace,
*Z*eroes more hopes

THAN ANY OTHER ENEMY OF MANKIND.

                    —The Huntington Central Christian.

APPENDIX

SOME QUESTIONS ABOUT DRINKING COMMONLY ASKED BY HIGH SCHOOL STUDENTS

(The answers are necessarily incomplete but may be somewhat amplified by the given references to other pages of this book)

Will drink injure me in my athletic training?

Yes, it radically affects your physical endurance, the speed of your reactions, etc. Charlie Justice, North Carolina's great triple-threat tailback and probably the greatest punter of all time, says: "I have never taken a drink of beer, liquor, or wine. Since my sandlot football days I've never played under a coach who tolerated drinking on the squad. I've never met a great athlete in any sport who cared to drink during the season or at any other time. You just can't participate in any sport unless your mind and body react perfectly for the quick decisions you must make. See p. 47.

Is whisky more harmful than beer?

Yes, because it is about 50% alcohol while beer is from 4 to 6%, and it is the amount of alcohol in a beverage that does the harm. However, a bottle of beer contains as much alcohol as a shot of whisky, and beer is usually taken in larger quantities which makes it almost equally harmful. And since beer can affect some persons as much as whisky does others, common sense would suggest that you substitute for it unfermented fruit juices or other soft drink. See p. 46.

How can I drink without becoming drunk or developing into a drunkard?

There is no definite recipe for this because the first drink impairs the judgment and conscience to a degree that makes the second drink seem desirable, and this may make the third drink irresistible; so that any rule of moderation one might beforehand adopt is easily overstepped. As alcohol is a habit-forming drug, a series of such oversteppings carries one easily on to alcoholism. Recent estimates show that one out of every sixteen who drink eventually becomes an addict; doctors have no way of telling which of the sixteen it would be. *It might be you!*

Why is drinking permitted?

Because society has not yet applied to alcohol the scientific and common sense criteria used in the case of morphine and other poisonous drugs or poisoned foods. This is due to the pleasurable but temporary and deceptive feeling of release and well-being which it brings about and its age-long association with hospitality, ceremonial customs and religious ritual.

Why do people drink?

At first because it has been customary in their environment to drink or because they unthinkingly drift into it or because they lack the courage, independence and maturity of judgment to resist the social pressure which assumes drinking to be the usual and desirable thing. Under this pressure it easily crystallizes into a habit; while some who suffer from suppressed personality disorders, deceived by the relief from tension, anxiety and self-consciousness they experience, resort to it more and more frequently and so glide gradually into alcoholism. See pp. 7, 15, 54.

Are there any diseases caused by drinking?

There is a close association between heavy drinking and such dietary diseases as beriberi and pellagra, and diseases of the liver, as well as various nervous disorders. See also pp. 41, 45, 96. Alcoholism itself is now called a disease.

Can I do more work if I drink?

In proportion to its extent drinking curtails endurance, control and coördination in physical effort, and judgment, accuracy and initiative in mental work. See pp. 33, 38, 40, 83, 84, 88, 113, 119, 144.

Will I be unpopular if I do not drink?

Not if you cultivate the constructive qualities of considerateness for others' interests and ideas, good sportsmanship and general leadership.

(The boys ask) *Will it be easier for me to get the girls to do what I want if they are drinking?*

Yes, if you want them to do something opposed to their idea of what is intelligent, right or fitting. But they will be less capable of joining in any rational sport or recreation.

(The girls ask) *Will boys like me as well if I drink?*

The better type of boy will not. See p. 64.

Will drinking make me fat?

Drinking, especially in excess, often produces a bleary, bloated appearance. See p. 63.

INDEX OF NAMES